KU-355-634

SAVE THE VILLAGE POND

Conservation
handbook of the
SAVE THE
VILLAGE POND
CAMPAIGN

British
Waterfowl
Association

Ford
Motor Company
Limited

Written by
JOHN DYSON

Design
JOHN BIGG

Colour illustration
JOHN RIGNALL

Line drawings
JOYCE TUHILL

Photographs
JOHN CLEGG
JOHN DYSON
FORD MOTOR COMPANY LTD
L. HUGH NEWMAN

Published by the
Ford Motor Company Ltd
© 1974

Cover picture:
Hinxworth village pond, Herts.

Opposite:
Top Northern pintail drake,
Mallard duck with ducklings.
Bottom (left to right) Fulvous
tree duck, Baikal teal drake,
Goldeneye drake, Shelduck
drake.

CONTENTS

POND RESTORATION

5 Give Nature a chance without crippling her, attend to the surroundings of the pond. Create the right conditions for wild or ornamental waterfowl, and fish, to inhabit the pond.

POND MANAGEMENT

6 A village pond is an ideal outdoor classroom for observing and studying Nature. The children themselves can help a lot to keep the pond in a tidy and healthy condition and by taking an interest are less inclined to cause accidental damage.

FIELD STUDIES

7 The story of how one village in Lincolnshire attempted the impossible and turned a local eyesore into a nature reserve and pond that won a Countryside Award is an inspiring example.

POND CASEBOOK

FOREWORD

The motor car has given greater freedom and mobility to more people than ever before to enjoy the countryside. It has also contributed to social changes which have altered the character of some aspects of that countryside. For example when the internal combustion engine took over from the horse, it removed one of the last functions of the village pond.

Once there were well over 300,000 ponds in Britain. They provided water for animals and often humans as well. A very large number are now rapidly silting up; becoming a dumping ground for old iron or overgrown with vegetation. Some are only recognisable as a patch of marshy ground. Many more will soon be like that. And yet, cleaned out and properly managed, they could not only be conserved but add to the beauty of Britain.

The British Waterfowl Association and Ford started to discuss a campaign to 'Save the Village Pond' in 1972. In the following two years we have had the benefit of advice, encouragement and considerable enthusiasm from many of the leading conservation and environmental groups, as well as individuals who have been consulted. We are grateful that their assistance has enabled us to produce this book and plan a campaign which we hope will have lasting ecological benefits as well as giving satisfaction to those who participate and pleasure to those who pass by the village pond.

Terry Beckett
Managing Director
Ford Motor Company Limited

INTRODUCTION

A victim of neglect, pollution and vandalism, the village pond is fast disappearing. For centuries it has played a fundamental role in rural life: its story is as long as the history of the village as a community. Now, with no role to play like those of other traditional village institutions such as the green and the pub, the pond is on the verge of extinction.

The few village ponds that can still be seen in good condition are vivid demonstrations of the need to halt the decay – people come from far and wide to see what is only a feature of traditional village life. Children feed the ducks, or fish for sticklebacks; birds such as swifts come down to find clay for their nests; dragonflies hover amid the reeds and whirligig beetles describe crazy patterns of ripples on the pond's still surface . . .

The capital cost of cleaning out a decaying pond and putting it back on the road to recovery is practically nothing. Restoring it for the amenity of the neighbourhood and the benefit of wildlife is expensive only in terms of effort and enthusiasm.

To kindle that enthusiasm, and to channel ideas and energy so that no community effort goes unrewarded, the British Waterfowl Association, sponsored by Ford Motor Company Ltd., has launched the SAVE THE VILLAGE POND CAMPAIGN.

Behind the running of the campaign is a committee of experts, including representatives from organisations such as the Association of County Naturalists' and Conservation Trusts (S.P.N.R.), the British Trust for Conservation Volunteers, the National Biological Records Centre of the Natural Environment Research Council, and the Council for the Protection of Rural England. Operating full-time from an office in London, to lend their experience and the benefit of their advice to any community doing something about its pond, are the Campaign's director, Mr Christopher Harrisson, and the deputy director, Mr Geoffrey Kidner.

A trophy for the best-kept pond which has been restored with the support of the SAVE THE VILLAGE POND CAMPAIGN will be presented annually. The trophy is being sponsored by The Daily Telegraph Limited. Details are available from the Campaign director.

A field pond (above) like this one is a rural beauty spot of inestimable value to the countryside. But without care it can become an eyesore and a hazard (right) which is soon filled in and grassed over.

HOW THE CAMPAIGN CAN HELP

The Save the Village Pond Campaign is aimed primarily at ponds to which the public has access. However, this book will also provide useful information for those who wish to restore or improve ponds on their own property.

1

Complete the survey card (see page 28) to record the present condition of your pond and send it with a covering letter to the Campaign office.

2

When possible the director, the deputy director, or an officer of the Campaign will visit the pond to advise on its capacity for restoration and to identify immediate practical problems and the cost of fixing them.

3

A survey of the pond by an expert naturalist will then be arranged, usually through the County Naturalists' or Conservation Trust, to ensure no rare species of flora or fauna will be endangered, and to advise on wildlife conservation.

4

Special problems such as polluted inflow of water or the height of the water table can be dealt with by local experts such as water engineers who can be contacted through the Campaign headquarters.

5

While the practical restoration work is done expert guidance will be given when required through a local representative of the National Conservation Corps.

6

If no adequate local volunteer labour force is available, the director can arrange for the National Conservation Corps to help in the work.

7

The Campaign will offer continuing advice on all aspects of pond management, including fish-stocking, introducing ornamental waterfowl, attracting wild duck, extending the pond, and how to keep the pond in good condition to conserve wildlife.

SAVE THE VILLAGE POND CAMPAIGN
111, Lambeth Road,
London SE1
Telephone: 01-582-0185

1

Discover the origin of the village pond and find out about its history. Identify the reasons why it has fallen into decay and disrepair.

THE STORY OF PONDS

THE VILLAGE FILLING STATION

The pond belongs at the heart of village life along with other traditional institutions such as the village green, the inn, and the church. From times when Roman highways rumbled to the tune of horse-drawn chariots, to the early decades of this century when traction engines and draught-horse teams gave up the unequal struggle against the motor vehicle, field ponds were the filling stations of the rural scene.

For nearly two thousand years ponds provided an essential service as watering places. Plough horses on their way to work in the fields, heavy horses hauling lumbering freight wagons, cattle and sheep being driven to and from market, cows on their way to milking, carriage horses, and horses being ridden – all broke their journeys at village ponds.

Where horses and stock paused to drink it was a natural consequence that riders, cart and carriage drivers, and drovers with their dogs required places to rest, eat, and chew the wad over rough ale. Because they were staging posts on cross-country journeys, ponds were often found at the intersections of rural highways, and around them grew up small service industries.

Whether a particular pond existed naturally and a village grew up around it, or villagers created a pond with which to water their stock, is a chicken-or-the-egg situation that only local historians can unravel. The countryside is full of examples of both situations.

Where ponds occurred naturally, roads and trackways tended to follow them. Many originated around springs which were tapped for the use of villagers and travellers. Even when a springhead of stones was built around the water source, the constant overflow and trampling could turn the surrounding area into a bog which was then contained and within a short time developed into a pond.

Some ponds were made by accident – a result of digging a pit for clay with which to build houses, perhaps – and were soon adapted to supply water. Others were created for specific purposes, such as keeping fish, attracting wild duck, making ice, curling, or providing a head of water with which to drive a mill wheel or a tilt hammer.

In the long hot summers that we don't seem to get these days, the wood of which cartwheels were made was prone to contract so the iron rims fell off. The pond was useful not only for cooling and refreshing the horses, but for standing carts and carriages so the wood swelled.

Some village ponds served the additional purpose of nursing a grove of willows which were used in the old days for making baskets, creels, and panniers. Willow 'spics' were also used for thatching, and building wattle and daub.

Village society was so cut off in Britain's rural backwaters that it was only in 1880 that the last known case of swimming a witch was recorded, at a village pond in Bedfordshire. For some three hundred years, swimming a witch was an integral part of country life and an outlet for mob passions.

The victim was bound in an awkward posture and thrown in the pond. If she floated, her survival was put down to the influence of Satan and she was condemned. If she sank she was judged innocent, but was most likely to be dead by the time she was fished out.

Lunatics, petty offenders, scolds and drunks were also taught a lesson with an occasional ducking in the village pond, and in some places a special 'ducking stool' was employed.

When steam engines chuffed their way from village to village, hauling heavy ploughing rigs and threshing tackle, progress was made from pond to pond so drivers could give their 'iron horses' a drink. Ponds also became important storage tanks for water in case of fire: the nearest pond was usually the only source of water available to the old-fashioned horse-drawn fire brigades.

Today, the village pond has no practical use. Few horses remain to drink at it; cows are watered by piped supply to troughs in the fields; the logistics of fire-fighting have largely been solved by underground mains; witch-hunting is a rather more civilised affair. Sadly, the days when a village pond could be drained and an old codger be overheard to say, 'There was carp in there as big as pig', are over.

In many villages the pond has become a communal waste-disposal unit. Pressure to have 'something done about it' grows rapidly. It is now too easy to find some contractor willing to pay for the privilege of dumping a few tons of rubble into a hole in the ground. A load of topsoil and a packet of grass seed completes the job.

WHERE PONDS COME FROM

The number of ponds that still exist can only be guessed at. No record is kept of how quickly ponds are disappearing. But some indication of the scale of the problem can be judged from the numbers of ponds recorded in the countryside as a whole and plotted on the two-and-a-half inches to the mile Ordnance Survey maps.

Counting bodies of water that are neither rivers nor obviously moats on a sample of maps, it has been calculated that there are 338,000 ponds in England and Wales.

However, the maps are now decades out of date, most having been surveyed between 1930 and 1960; checking on the ground has shown that many ponds were overlooked either because they were too small, concealed by woodland, or happened to be dry at the time.

Ponds tend to be commonest in the lowland counties of England and in the parts of the country which were first to be enclosed, in or before the sixteenth and early seventeenth centuries. About a quarter of all ponds on the sample maps occurred in Norfolk and Cheshire; about a quarter occurred in the hill-farm country of Devon and Cornwall, the North, and Wales. And the remaining half were in the other lowland counties. Only a very small proportion were in villages. But a great many either can be seen from the road, are linked by ancient trackways or bridle paths that are now public footpaths, or in various ways are accessible to the general public.

In the countryside now, ponds are simply a waste of land. Look at just one factor causing ponds to disappear: in 1880 a 500-acre farm in west Wiltshire had no piped water supply, and 133 acres of its pasture depended on ponds for watering cattle in summer. In 1960, nearly the whole farm – 485 acres – was supplied with piped water and not a single pond remained.

Many such ponds were either dug specially to drain the field as well as supply water, or as 'marl' pits, usually by wandering bands of labourers who specialised in such work. Marling was undertaken when the sandy topsoil proved to be of poor quality. Pits were dug in the chalk or clay and this was spread over the surface of the field then ploughed in to improve the fertility.

Drinking ponds were required in great numbers when the Parliamentary Acts of Enclosure reduced the huge open fields of the Midlands, many of them several hundred acres in extent, to a number of small regularly-shaped fields bounded by hawthorn hedges that give today's countryside its familiar 'counterpane'

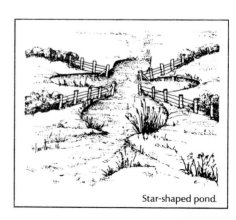

Star-shaped pond.

appearance.

In some areas artificial cattle-drinking ponds were constructed with four arms so that one pond served four different fields. However, some star-shaped ponds occurred for other reasons because examples have been found in woodland that has never been cultivated.

When the massive cloak of glaciated ice rolled back at the end of the last Ice Age, a wild landscape of hillocks and muddy hollows was left behind. This was gradually smoothed down by thousands of years of wind, rain and sunshine until today's undulating landscape was formed. The deepest hollows filled with water to provide ponds.

On chalk lands there are natural ponds and lakes caused by 'solution hollows' where the chalk was dissolved by the ground water until the surface caved in.

Another type of natural pond is the 'pingo', a Finnish word given to a pond created in the perma-frost conditions of the Ice Age. Below ground level the soil was permanently frozen. Water seepage caused pressure to build up so the surface was pushed upwards, creating a hill which was covered with vegetation. When the climate grew warmer the core of ice inside the mound melted and the hill collapsed, forming a pond.

Much legend surrounds the large, circular 'dew ponds' which are found mainly in fields, but also occasionally in villages, on the high, chalk sheep-grazing downs of Sussex, Wiltshire, Berkshire, Dorset, and parts of Yorkshire, and Hertfordshire.

Also known as 'cloud' or 'mist' ponds,

they were credited with magical qualities and were said never to run dry, even during the hottest summers. Country folk had a theory that they were of miraculous origin, were filled by God, and that their name was more correctly *Dieu* pond.

Some dew ponds are undoubtedly very old and may go back to Anglo Saxon or even British-Roman times, as is the case at Ashmore, Dorset, where the village is built around the edge of a beautiful round dew pond on the 700-foot contour of Cranborne Chase. The mysterious quality of these ponds has been a source of conjecture for centuries. What is almost certain is that dew ponds are not significantly replenished by dew, although condensation probably contributes.

They were built to order by specialist craftsmen as late as the 1930s. Far from the secret of their construction being closely guarded between father and son, or lost with the passing of Neolithic Man as some country tales would have us believe, there are at least twenty-three different ways of constructing a dew pond.

The site chosen was a 'cold spot' where the lie of the surrounding hills tended to concentrate mists and wisps of low cloud, and where rain-water run-off was channelled. A wide and shallow saucer-shaped hole was dug and the banks built up to increase the catchment as much as possible. Because chalk is porous the pond was lined with clay which was 'puddled' or trampled so it formed a dense waterproof layer without any fissures.

TRACING HISTORY

Pursuing the story of a village pond is a challenge to local historians because so few studies have ever been made. Whatever the origin of a village pond, it was nearly always modified by later use. Hard historical evidence is practically non-existent. Even modern books about village life, farming, rural England, and practical history make scant reference to ponds despite the fact that they performed such a vital service in the rural community. In ancient documents, reference is even rarer.

In pre-Roman times wells were not dug so prehistoric man depended on streams, springs and ponds. Some of those ponds still survive, if only as earthworks, and have long since dried up, but some are still in use. It is possible that the history of a pond could cover nearly 2000 years.

Archaeological investigations of ponds have been few; little is known of ponds built before the Middle Ages beyond the fact that some very old ponds do exist. Excavations of such ponds on the downs

have shown that they were cleaned out regularly. It is suspected that when they built roads the Romans drained them into ponds and in so doing provided watering places for horses and livestock using the route.

Often the first clue to a pond's history is in the name. The Anglo Saxons had many names for different types of ponds but the most common was *mere*, which was also applied to natural lakes and sometimes the sea.

The word 'pond' itself appeared in Old English only in composition, the commonest form being *pund-fald* – a pind-fold, or pen, in which animals were herded. Its application to water became common only after the Norman Conquest when it described water 'pounded' behind dams to form millponds and fishponds.

Although references to ponds in historic documents are rare, they do turn up from time to time in the Anglo Saxon bound marks recorded in the eighth, ninth and tenth centuries. When parish

A farm moat: defence against cattle rustlers.

boundaries were drawn up they sometimes converged on a pond so the water was shared by people of several parishes; the historian can then determine that the date of the pond was prior to the defining of boundaries.

Early maps are one of the best sources of early information on ponds because some were drawn in great detail, to a high standard of cartography, and on scales as much as twenty-five inches to the mile which showed every tree and every building, as well as ponds. The maps usually covered estates or parishes and if looked out in county records a lot can be gleaned from them.

Ponds are also occasionally referred to in medieval documents, such as accounts of people being drowned in them, reports of offences such as illicit fishing being dealt with by manorial courts, and agricultural leases in which marling was stipulated as a condition.

One of the main clues to the origins of a pond is how the material that came out of it was disposed of. If the pond has no banks and rather steep sides it may have been created for some purpose other than that of watering stock, though it may have been used for that later on.

Many ponds originate from pits dug out in the search for clay with which to make bricks, construct railway embankments, and build houses. From Anglo-Saxon times until well into the nineteenth century houses were built of wattle and daub, of which the main constituent was clay. It is likely that a pond furnished material for building several such houses and may well be situated equidistant between them.

In Staffordshire and the Weald a lot of ponds were made by damming streams to provide a head of water for driving waterwheels which in turn drove tilt-hammers or other machinery used in iron-smelting or glass-making. The 'hammer' ponds occurred mainly in remote areas and usually in woods because iron-smelting depended on charcoal. But some gave rise to villages that adopted the word 'hammer' in their names and the ponds frequently still exist.

In parts of the West Country growan (a kind of 'rotten' granite also known as cob) was dug out of the ground for building houses. The pits filled with water and can still be seen on the upland plateaux, but the houses built of the material are in the valleys.

Ponds were adapted to later uses in many different ways – as drinking troughs, duck decoys (for catching wild duck to sell in the cities), and as fish ponds. Some ponds were known as 'stew ponds' because their purpose was to hold the fish that in Catholic households was consumed on Fridays. Ponds specifically built for fish breeding usually lay under the eye of the manor, where they could be guarded against poachers, and comprised a number of small ponds in which different sizes of fish, and different types, were raised.

In north-west Essex, west Suffolk and west Cambridge the number of moats runs into thousands. They can be seen in villages that were originally hamlets or lonely farms, or in positions where isolated farms once existed.

HOW PONDS CHOKE TO DEATH

The village pond's function of providing drinking water for stock and horses was eliminated by several different factors. Horses as an essential means of transport disappeared from the rural scene almost overnight; those that remained were watered in farmyard drinking troughs.

Cattle, dairy herds and sheep that by custom were watered at the village pond once or twice a day were saved the journey by the wide introduction of water piped directly to drinking troughs in fields. Farmers could get financial assistance from the Government to cover most of the capital cost.

Ducks and geese which formerly roamed the village green and kept the pond clear of weeds were affected more and more by traffic so villagers were inclined to keep them enclosed.

Once the practical use of ponds was removed people stopped caring about them. A shallow pond left to itself soon reverts to a marshy area; marginal plants such as reedmace spread across more and more of the pond until the whole thing is choked.

At the same time as the revolution of modern agriculture sounded the death knell of the pond as a source of drinking water, the rise in standards of living between the wars brought the flushing WC to thousands of cottages. They were introduced before any drainage scheme or sewer disposal 'main' had been installed, and drained into a cess pit with an overflow into a ditch. The inevitable result was that ponds became polluted and, in dry summers particularly, smelled unpleasant.

Road widening schemes and demands for car-parking caused many ponds to be filled in, particularly when they were situated near a cross-roads where carriageways had to be widened to allow safer traffic behaviour to be engineered, or when they stood opposite a village pub whose customers cluttered the lane with their cars.

Sixty years ago it would have required half-a-dozen men with wheelbarrows and horse-drawn carts working for a week to fill in a village pond. Today, a tip-truck can do the job in a single morning and contractors will frequently pay for the privilege of disposing of a load of unwanted rubble or spoil.

One of the unwritten bye-laws of the consumer society is that there seem to be no holds barred when it comes to getting rid of one's rubbish. A village pond provides one of the most convenient waste disposal units in the countryside because there is only a single splash, a ripple in the reeds, and all signs of the offence are eliminated within seconds. If it were a matter of only a few bottles being thrown into the pond the problem would not be so serious. When tins are thrown in, the metals leach poison into the water and these kill off small creatures on which fish and birds depend for food. Then there is nothing to prevent weeds from spreading over the surface.

Some sources of pollution that cause village ponds to be stagnant are less obvious. But they are more insidious and in some respects are harder to cope with.

Fertilisers used in large quantities on fields, and weed-killers and pest

Festering with rubbish, this pond is on the point of total ruin.

controllers, leach out of the fields into the drains and inevitably find their way to ponds where their concentrations are increased.

Road drains, too, are often linked to ponds. After a long spell of dry weather the detritus of rubber and oil on the roads builds up until the first good rainstorm washes it away into the village pond where it forms a toxic film on the surface of the water. The scale of the disaster is as devastating to the pond as the pollution of the Devon and Cornish beaches by the *Torrey Canyon*. When a road is re-sealed the petroleum spirit washed out of the tar can kill a pond overnight and recovery can take a year.

Pollution of pond water can also occur through natural causes. When a lot of leaves fall into a pond, from brambles and shrubs on the banks or from overhanging trees, the process of decomposition uses up all the available oxygen. Living creatures and plants die off because they are starved of oxygen. If a pond is filled or topped up by outflow from a farmyard the same problem can occur, because the water is over-enriched by the content of dung and vegetable matter: the water takes on the appearance of green soup owing to the presence of myriads of algae.

Pond creatures have a natural defence against natural hazards, such as hot summers that cause the pond to dry out temporarily, or bad winters that sheath the pond in ice for long periods. Against chemicals they have no resilience.

2

Establish who owns the pond. Seek the blessing, and the active participation, of the local council. If necessary, form a group and present a strong case to the annual village meeting. Protect the pond against those who dump rubbish, and vandals.

VILLAGE ACTION

PUTTING THE CASE

Spring and early summer is the ideal time to get action going on the restoration of a village pond. Not because that is ideal from the conservation point of view – autumn and winter are better for getting down to work. But in England, the annual meeting of the local* council must be held between March 1 and June 1. At this meeting any village resident is entitled to speak, suggest what action to take, and vote. In Wales, any six electors can convene a community meeting.

The simple way to start is to write to the clerk of the council in advance and explain that you wish to table a motion at the annual meeting 'urging the council to investigate the village pond with a view to restoring it'.

An annual meeting is likely to be lively if another lobby in the village is pressing to have the pond filled in because it is smelly, a health hazard, or presents a risk to children. If this is likely to occur it is important to be forewarned so that a well reasoned case can be made for restoring the pond and managing it for the villagers as well as for wildlife.

The case will seem more impressive if you can put forward a complete management plan. The Save the Village Pond Campaign will offer advice.

The first step is to establish

*After April 1, 1974, parish councils in England become local councils; parish councils in Wales become community councils. Throughout this book, parish councils and their equivalents are referred to as local councils.

ownership. If the pond is owned or managed by the council it may be persuaded to allow a responsible group to take a hand in looking after the pond and restoring it.

If the pond is privately owned, the restoration venture will be helped if it has the council's blessing. It is likely that a farmer, the brewery which happens to own the pub, or the Lord of the Manor, owns the pond and might be only too pleased to sell it for a small sum or lease it for a token amount.

Initially, a council may well have reservations about putting effort and money (no matter how little) into what it sees only as a bit of bog filled with rubbish. Or else it will adamantly refuse to agree that such a village eyesore could ever be restored, and now that the pond's deplorable state has come to its attention may fill it in.

To counter this, some old-fashioned political lobbying of the councillors, and propaganda making use of colour slides, newspaper articles, film shows, or visits to a nearby pond that has already been restored, may prove helpful.

When putting the case, the main points are:

Amenity A well-kept pond is charming and pretty; residents and visitors alike will benefit; the village will become more desirable as a place to live.

Safety Small boys and ponds have co-existed for hundreds of years with remarkably few accidents; low banks and a graded pond bottom will ensure that anybody who falls in could walk out.

Conservation Every community has a clear duty to preserve the environment for future generations; a well-managed pond is a miniature nature reserve of prime importance.

Education A pond is an ideal outdoor classroom for all ages of children; local children can use the pond for field studies and assist in its maintenance; vandalism, whether intentional or otherwise, will be reduced.

Smell A healthy pond does not smell unpleasant and presents no hazard to public health.

Rubbish It is proven that commons and village ponds kept in good condition do not attract illegal dumping.

Cost Restoration of ponds demands energy and enthusiasm and lots of volunteers; cost could be as low as ten pounds and is seldom more than fifty.

Apart from the Save the Village Pond Campaign and County Naturalists' or Conservation Trusts, support for the scheme should be solicited from as many local organisations as possible, including local land-owners and farmers, Young Farmers' clubs, political groups, village societies and clubs of any description.

Traditionally, villages are sleepy hollows. In fact, a high proportion comprise commuters who are skilled in professional fields and all can play an important role in pressing for the improvement of their village.

Active support should also be solicited from local farmers, foresters and builders – for their practical advice, because they may be the only people in the village who are still actively concerned with the management of land, and for the equipment they may be persuaded to lend to a band of volunteer workers.

ROLE OF THE LOCAL COUNCIL

There is nothing in legislation to prevent a local council from undertaking pond restoration itself, or allowing it to be done – if necessary under its control – by volunteers. If the council already owns or manages the pond and the land surrounding it, any restoration project will require its full approval.

When the land is not owned or managed by the council, and it shows no interest in the reclamation of the pond, a group of volunteers or a village society can get on with it independently as long as their work neither interferes with the road nor constitutes any sort of hazard.

There are several headings under which a council can assist volunteer effort by apportioning funds from the general rates, and underwriting the cost of equipment.

Under its statutory powers the council '. . . may clean out ponds, ditches and drains and may utilise any well, spring or stream in its area and may provide facilities for obtaining water therefrom and may execute works but not so as to interfere with any private right'.

This could cover the cost of a suction pump, for example, or a sludge gulper for removing the sludge from the pond and disposing of it.

A council could help by taking care of the peripheral areas of a pond. In the general interest of amenity it is entitled to provide shelters and seats at public places, provide public conveniences, and install litter bins as long as arrangements are made for disposing of their contents. It can lay out grass verges, plant them with trees and shrubs, and maintain guards or fences to protect them.

The council may contribute to expenses of certain kinds incurred by other bodies such as village societies or clubs. These can include the acquisition of rights of way, pleasure boats, recreation grounds, village greens, commons, and entertainment in practically any context.

It can buy land under the rule which states that lands may be acquired and equipped '. . . for the use of clubs and organisations having athletic, social and educational objects'. A natural history club, for example, could fall within the definition of both 'social' and 'educational'. A village society formed expressly for restoring and managing its pond could define its activities in such a way that a sympathetic council would not be prevented from buying the pond and the land around it.

The district council and the local council each have the general power to deal with pieces of water which have become offensive or injurious to health. There is no limit to the amount of money that can be spent on making a pond efficient and getting it straight, including planting grass, trees and shrubs, and creating proper banks.

To go one stage further and manage the pond in a way that is ideal for wildlife, or to make it look beautiful, is unlikely to be costly. Should money be required, the council can spend money on it only according to the terms under which the land is held.

If the land is a recreation ground – and recreation can include such things as sailing model boats – the council has powers under section 8 of the Local

Government Act of 1894 to spend money on its maintenance and improvement.

If the land is held under the Open Spaces Act of 1906, it is empowered under section 10 to spend what it likes to . . .

'(a) hold and administer it in trust to allow, and with a view to, the enjoyment thereof by the public as an open space;

(b) maintain and keep it in a good and decent state, and may inclose it or keep it enclosed with proper railings and gates, and may drain, level, lay out, turf, plant, ornament, light, provide with seats and otherwise improve it, and do all such work and things and employ such officers and servants as may be requisite for the purposes aforesaid of any of them.'

This Edwardian act may be decidedly vague, but empowers much general activity on open areas. Under it, the council may also carry out the maintenance and improvements as specified of practically any piece of land it agrees to take over and manage as a public open space.

In effect, this means that a land-owner who is persuaded to part with his pond so it can be restored and used by the village merely has to exchange letters with the council for any necessary work to be carried out on it and for the public to have right of access. Section 9 of the Act says a local authority may . . .

(a) acquire by agreement and for valuable or nominal consideration by way of payment, or without any consideration, the freehold of, or any term of years, or any interest in any open space, whether situate within the district of the local authority or not; and

(b) undertake the entire or partial care, management and control; and

(c) for the purposes aforesaid, make any agreement with any person. . . .

If a council feels that restoration of its pond is a special project that is really beyond its usual brief, it can raise extra money from the rates to cover the cost.

In the past, the law was that all local authorities could spend money raised through rates only on activities that were expressly authorised by Parliament. This proved restrictive to local authorities that attempted to be enterprising, because any ratepayer could challenge the council on grounds that it was exceeding its responsibility.

Parliament in 1963 agreed that one-fifth of a penny rate could be spent by councils on practically anything that would benefit the neighbourhood. Known as the 'free fifth' it was being increased on 1st April 1974 to a 'free two-penny' rate which the council can spend to finance a particular project.

In very small parishes where the free fifth brought in only about £5, a sum of £50 could now be expected. In most parishes or communities, the free two-pence would raise at least £350 if it were levied, while in some very large parishes a rate of only one penny could yield as much as £60,000.

The money may be used for any expenditure which, in the *council's opinion*, is in the interests of its area, or any part of it, or all or some of its inhabitants.

PONDS ON GREENS AND COMMONS

The status of the village green goes back to the earliest days of the village as a community, to Britain's 'frontier days' of medieval history when it played its part in the defence of the village and the protection of live-stock.

The village butts for archery practice were set up on the green. If the Battle of Waterloo was won on the playing fields of Eton, the decisive battles of Crécy, Poitiers and Agincourt were undoubtedly won on the village greens of England.

There are 1,383 village greens in England and Wales, averaging about three acres in size. They are more characteristic of the Home Counties and the eastern side of England generally. Many village greens include ponds.

Commons are the remnant of the manorial system which was the basis of the country's economic life in the Middle Ages.

In the middle of the last century thousands of acres of common land were enclosed. One benefit, however, was that small areas were allotted for such public uses as gravel digging, the site of a poorhouse, and the recreation of the inhabitants. In this way, part of a common became used as a village green.

Village greens usually belong to the local council. If no owner has been found, the council manages the land. Therefore, it is unlikely that any attempts to work on a pond that is situated on a village green would be successful without the council's full support and active interest.

Today, common land totals about one and a half million acres in England and Wales. Most of it occurs on tussocky uplands, but half the lowland commons of England lie within fifty miles of London and are now subject to considerable public pressure for recreation. Many such commons include one or more ponds.

While a green is essentially a piece of land for the village, a common is quite different. It is a piece of land, including any water such as a pond, over which certain people have rights. These can include: Common in the soil (the right to take sand, gravel); pannage (the right to let pigs enter a wood to eat acorns or beech-mast); estovers (the right to take small branches for firewood and bracken for cattle bedding); turbary (the right to dig turf or peat for fuel, an action which often creates ponds); and piscary (the right to fish for one's own consumption).

By far the most usual is common of pasture – the right to graze stock.

The owner of the common may well have different rights, such as shooting, timber felling, and excavating minerals. He may also prosecute trespassers but he is not allowed to fence the common.

Under the Commons Registration Act of 1965 all commons and greens must be registered. Records are kept at County and District Records Offices. The registrations are plotted on large-scale maps. Owners of the land, and the names and addresses of those who have common rights, are listed. A pond on a common may well have piscary rights, and the holders of those rights would have to be approached before any work could start. Commons are sometimes administered by a committee of those who hold rights.

PROTECTING THE POND

Once the pond is restored, earnest efforts by villagers will be required to keep it tidy and prevent it from falling into disrepair. When things are kept in good order, and look as if they are cared for, they tend not to attract vandals.

A pond on a busy road is an open invitation to litter dumping and the only way to prevent it is to keep a good look out. Those who live nearby ought to be approached to keep a special eye open. Volunteer wardens to keep the place tidy, and to be on hand to prevent damage at busy times such as Sunday afternoons, should be enlisted.

When a person dumping litter is confronted, he is entitled to refuse to give his name and address. If he is a local person he is probably known, if not he will most likely have arrived by car whose registration number can be traced. When vandals or dumpers are spotted, get names and addresses of as many witnesses as you can.

The Police may well show little interest in the case, because they have more important things to do. The local council, however, has a general authority to spend money prosecuting summary offenders.

In some circumstances the pond can be placed under the umbrella protection of bye-laws which regulate general activity over the pond area, such as preventing harassment of waterfowl. Bye-laws should be clearly posted nearby. The maximum penalty for infringement is then a fine of £20. Bye-laws are not necessary to control damage or dumping, which are covered under general law; the penalties are much higher. A vandal might be prosecuted under the Criminal Damage Act of 1971, for which the penalty is a fine of up to £400 and the right to compensation. Those who throw rubbish in the pond may be prosecuted under the Dangerous Litter Act of 1971, for which the maximum fine is £100. If the dumping of rubbish also leads to the serious pollution of the pond waters, it is possible that the offender could be prosecuted under the Criminal Damage Act and compensation to cover cost of repairs could be pressed for.

If the land on which a pond stands was acquired by the council under the Open Spaces Act of 1906, or if the council already owns the land and it has been designated a recreational space under the public health acts, the council can make bye-laws with the approval of the Home Office.

If the pond stands on a green or a common which is already covered by bye-laws, they will almost certainly cover the pond; if necessary, additional ones can be added.

The Home Office model bye-laws warn councils that . . . 'It is doubtful whether grounds where the public are subject to a multitude of bye-laws are better managed than those where reliance is placed on the general law and ordinary good feeling.' When a pond is seriously affected by road widening it is possible that the whole pond can be moved. As road-building machinery will be on site in any case, the cost will be minimal. Water plants and animals can be offered temporary accommodation in aquaria, perhaps by the local school.

3

ECOLOGY OF STILL WATERS

Carry out an eco-survey to establish whether the pond is important to wildlife and learn to identify the plants and animals that inhabit the pond; complete the record card of ecological data for the Save the Village Pond Campaign.

POND LIFE

Although it is often quite small, a pond is a very rich habitat. Many of the flora and fauna of a pond do not occur elsewhere. The number of animal species alone runs into hundreds – perhaps more than a thousand if microscopic species are included. Representatives of nearly every major group of the animal kingdom, except star-fish and sea urchins which live only in the sea, can be found in British ponds.

The mere presence of such a diversity of wildlife in and around a pond justifies its conservation. But there is an additional reason: the plants and animals in a pond comprise an almost self-contained community. Village ponds provide one of the best possible classrooms for studying the inter-relation of plants and animals and their environment.

Although the diversity and abundance of plants and animals is striking, they lead a knife-edge existence for their habitat is sensitive to rapid changes. Ponds are usually well sheltered and their water remains very still. Sunlight penetrates to the shallow bottom allowing weeds and plants to grow thickly, further reducing circulation of water. Because of the numbers of plants and the stillness of the water, oxygen is at a premium. During nights oxygen may be almost exhausted, and only when light returns, allowing plants to begin photosynthesising again, are animals rescued from suffocation.

A heavy rainstorm can flood a pond, dramatically altering its chemical content by diluting it. A hard frost can freeze it solid. In dry weather it may disappear. One still warm night when a big crop of algae is dying may lead to deoxygenation. Because conditions vary so rapidly, serious scientific study of pond life has been limited. Fresh-water biologists concentrate on lakes and rivers, which are more stable. Ponds tend to be avoided.

Ponds are among the few surviving habitats for many rare species of flowers that grow on wetlands. Dragonflies depend on ponds and other still waters for survival; of twenty-seven species of dragonfly in Britain, eight are in danger of being wiped out. Frogs have become rare in many parts of England, partly because ponds have disappeared.

Plants that live wholly in water do not need to support themselves like land plants, and when taken out of the water hang limply with all their beauty lost. Their roots serve only as anchors and they are kept buoyant by little cells filled with air, like lifejackets. As well as flowers they develop water buds which sink to the bottom until spring, or they reproduce vegetatively – if a piece breaks off it will just grow.

In any good pond there is a distinctive zonation – submerged plants such as pondweeds, floating plants, such as water-lilies, emergent plants which are rooted in water but grow above its surface, such as reeds and bulrushes, and bankside plants such as rushes which thrive in damp soil.

The excitement of life beneath the surface of a pond cannot be put into context unless you imagine yourself to be an inch high – or, to put it another way, multiply the size of everything else by seventy-two. The weeds would stand like trees, twenty to sixty feet above your head; their smooth trunks would curve slightly, and interlace to form a canopy. Darting in among them would be creatures as big as eagles – water-fleas. A fish would glide overhead like a ponderous airship and if it were a pike you would hide for dear life. Fresh-water shrimps, six feet long, would snap and snarl as you disturbed them, and dozens of nymphs about the same size would

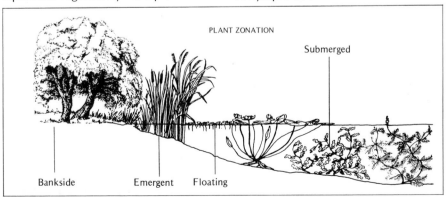

PLANT ZONATION

Submerged

Bankside   Emergent   Floating

HUNTERS AND THE HUNTED

lie around in weirdly shaped cases, like sleeping bags.

Once you started exploring you would give a wide berth to the shadow cast by a large red dragon fly, ten feet long, whose feet could be seen gripping a leaf just beneath the surface. As a nymph, it has a lower lip which is likely to shoot out like a tentacled pincer and the two teeth on the end of it would be powerful enough to grab and crush you.

Nimbleness and good cover is sufficient protection but you would wish for the greater field of view that most insects have, not that even better eyesight would help if you are unlucky enough to be sighted by a water beetle which would be twice your size. To be attacked would be like warding off a flying combine harvester.

You would watch where you stepped because lying half-hidden in the soft debris of the pond bottom would be ten-foot alder fly larva which snap like crocodiles. Snails would shoulder past with the relentless power of Stonehenge boulders on the move; newts would terrify, like dinosaurs; swan mussels would lie around like captured flying saucers and if you put your foot in one it would be bitten off.

When pond life is seen in these terms its conservation seems at least as important as the conservation of pandas, tigers, and other threatened species of animal and plant life.

A pond is a dangerous place if you happen to be only a few millimetres long. Life in the water is a constant search for something to eat – without being eaten. And if you lie quietly on the bank without moving, and peer down into a shallow area of clear water containing weed, you will see the whole pattern of 'hunt and be hunted' being enacted.

It is because a pond is an almost completely self-contained eco-system that it is so interesting; the intruders are birds, which feed on fish, insects, molluscs and plants, and nest on the banks. The only services they render are the control of certain weeds, (which is not always a good thing) and the unintentional carrying of plant seeds to other ponds.

Plants serve several vital functions in a pond. They must be positioned to use sunshine for photo-synthesis and so oxygenate the water. They provide shade and cover for the myriads of insects and animals that make homes among their stems and roots, and offer a ladder to the open air for nymphs.

Many animals feed on detritus, the small pieces of disintegrating plants and dead animals which litter the bottom of any pond. Carnivorous insects can be divided between those which lie in wait for their prey, and those which chase it – the lurkers and the hunters. Beetles are hunters, but if they don't guard their backs they are likely to be snapped up by something bigger than themselves.

At its simplest, the food chain in a pond begins with microscopic plants which float about in the water. These are eaten by microscopic animals, which

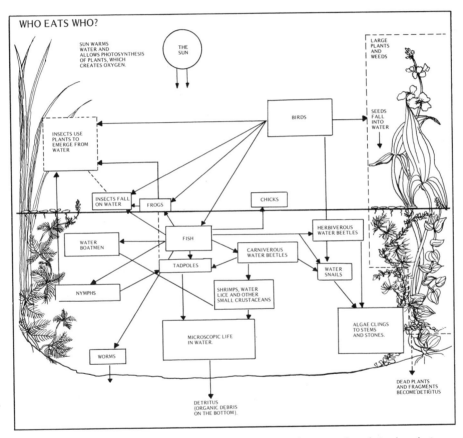

WHO EATS WHO?

SUN WARMS WATER AND ALLOWS PHOTOSYNTHESIS OF PLANTS, WHICH CREATES OXYGEN.

THE SUN

LARGE PLANTS AND WEEDS

BIRDS

SEEDS FALL INTO WATER

INSECTS USE PLANTS TO EMERGE FROM WATER

INSECTS FALL ON WATER

FROGS

CHICKS

HERBIVEROUS WATER BEETLES

WATER BOATMEN

FISH

CARNIVEROUS WATER BEETLES

WATER SNAILS

TADPOLES

NYMPHS

SHRIMPS, WATER LICE AND OTHER SMALL CRUSTACEANS

MICROSCOPIC LIFE IN WATER.

ALGAE CLINGS TO STEMS AND STONES.

WORMS

DEAD PLANTS AND FRAGMENTS BECOME DETRITUS

DETRITUS (ORGANIC DEBRIS ON THE BOTTOM).

in turn provide a diet for small animals and insects. Bigger animals feed on the small ones, and are gobbled up by fish which are eaten by water birds. The whole process is fuelled by sunshine, oxygen, and gases such as carbon dioxide in the water, which create the right conditions for the microscopic plants to reproduce very quickly.

When there is a break in the chain the whole system collapses. Oxygen level of a pond if critical. Decomposition of organic material such as fallen leaves consumes oxygen, reducing the supply available for living creatures. Trees around a pond can also break the chain by shading the light which plants need for photosynthesis.

27

A POND ECO-SURVEY

No work on a pond should begin without a thorough investigation and survey of the natural species of plants and animals that already live in and around it.

Great damage could be caused with the best intentions. For example, a pond could be an important breeding ground for frogs, because its shallow waters are ideal for spawning. To dig the pond out might drive the frogs away If ducks were introduced the spawn would be eaten.

It is only too easy to disturb a species that has not been noticed, despite careful investigation over several visits to a pond. In the south of England a pond that supported ten species of dragonfly nymphs would be extremely valuable, and any interference with the vegetation could upset the critical balance which makes conditions ideal.

Further north, where conditions are harsher, two or three species of dragonfly might warrant special treatment of a pond in order to conserve them. It is easily possible to visit a pond several times and not see even one of the dragonflies that exist there.

Name of pond: *Ponderton Hollow, Wessex*

Situation: *Half mile from Ponderton Church on the B.7673*

Grid ref: *436637*

Length: *65 ft*   Max. depth: *2 ft*   Avg. depth: *½ ft*

Water inflow: *Road and rain*   outflow: *Seepage*

Approx. total number of waterfowl that use pond: *None*

Name and address of owner (if known): *Ponderton Local Council High Street, Ponderton*   date: *12 – 3 – 74*

Description: Green   Common   Roadside   Field   Park
Woodland   Quarry

Access: Public   Private   Right of way   School   Part public

Uses: Fishing   Water sport   Picnics   Boating   Toy boats
Game rearing   None   Abandoned

Condition: Clean   Stagnant   Green   Refuse-fouled
Oil-fouled   Vegetation-clogged

Origin (if known): *Old horse pond last cleaned out in 1963 by mechanical shovel*

Please return this card to Save the Village Pond Campaign.

MAP

Draw shape of pond, including any island, nearby road, house, fence, car park, path

Floating plants   Marginal plants
Emergent plants   Greensward
Submerged plants   Trees (NAME)
×××× Shrubs and brambles ××××

Comments: *Parish Council intend to fill it in this summer because of rubbish*

Name of Surveyor: *John Smith*

Address: *16. Pond Lane, Ponderton, Wessex*

The eco-survey card is shown here in completed form.

Inconspicuous plants are easily damaged unintentionally. The water violet and the frog-bit sink to the bottom during the winter months, and any cleaning operation could eliminate some of the few surviving examples of what are two severely threatened species.

A wisp of green vegetation floating on the water may prove to be a rare water fern. There are even rare species of duckweed that only a knowledgeable botanist would recognise, and if it was decided to remove it, several rare species might be lost.

The Save the Village Pond Campaign (see page nine) is geared to advise on how to obtain this kind of specialist assistance. In most cases, the county naturalists' or conservation trusts or natural history societies will undertake this work. If a rare species exists, it will advise on how the pond should be managed to preserve the habitat.

At the same time, it is useful to undertake your own eco-survey of the pond. It will put on record the condition of the pond before any work is started. Subsequent improvements can be measured by repeating the survey and using the first as an index. Photographs should also be taken at every stage.

A simple survey can be carried out in the course of an afternoon by any person with an interest in natural history; a knowledge of the subject is not essential.

The eco-survey card which is enclosed with this handbook should be completed before any work is done to the pond, and forwarded to the Save the Village Pond Campaign.

Your own records could be kept in the same form, or a much more elaborate list of species could be drawn up with the advice of a naturalist.

Start the survey by noting the larger species of bird before they are frightened away, then work progressively from larger to smaller vegetation. Search for underwater creatures before disturbing the underwater plants. Return all specimens to the water.

The sketch map should indicate the approximate shape of the pond, its size, and the proportion of its area that is covered by weeds, emergent plants, or shadowed by trees. If there are fish in the pond, local anglers will know what species they are.

The depth of the pond can be measured with a pole, and its circumference estimated, or measured by a steel tape. Do not wade in the water without first making a careful survey of its depth.

When repeating a survey it is important to do it at the same time of year and in the same manner. If the population of a certain species, such as water boatmen, is being used as a comparative measure of the pond's health, it is important to carry out the same number of sweeps with a net over the same length of water and in the same conditions.

EQUIPMENT FOR PONDING

Finding out what lives in your pond begins with the selection of equipment suitable for catching tiny pond creatures without damaging them or their environment. Equipment is simple, cheap, and can be made or obtained at home:

Boots Suitable rubber boots are desirable for ponding unless the bottom is very clean.

White tray A plastic washing-up bowl or darkroom tray should be filled with about one inch of clean water in which to empty the net and sort the specimens.

Small trays Smaller trays such as enamel pie dishes, white so the animals can be seen easily, are handy for temporarily holding specimens that are being sorted.

Forceps For picking up beetles and bigger specimens.

Small jars Handy for holding specimens, but screw-top lids must be punctured so the specimens can breathe.

Old spoon For handling specimens.

Water-colour paintbrush For lifting out soft larvae and washing out into collecting jars.

Binoculars For watching birds.

Notebook and pencil For recording observations.

Pond net. The pond net must have a stout wooden handle, such as a broom handle, about six feet long. The wire hoop, which supports the net, should be rust-proof. A square shape is better for getting under stones and scraping along the bottom. The net should be about twelve inches deep. The best material is white nylon curtain, with a mesh of about one millimetre. Cheese-cloth, linen, or calico does not let the water pass through quickly enough. The upper hem enclosing the wire should be reinforced with a strip of stout material.

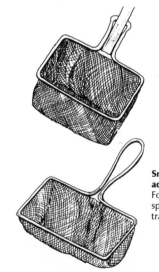

Small nylon aquarium net For re-catching specimens in trays or bowls.

Mud net A domestic flour sieve with a metal mesh is more rigid than a net made of fabric and can be used for scooping out creatures that live in the mud.

Glass-bottomed box For observing creatures in their natural surroundings.

Plastic bags Useful for transporting specimens for they can be filled with a little water and tied.

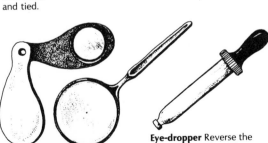

Pocket lens or magnifying glass For studying specimens.

Eye-dropper Reverse the glass tube so the wide end of the dropper can be used.

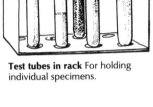

Test tubes in rack For holding individual specimens.

Sticky labels For labelling and numbering specimens.

Sounding stick Any long pole is necessary for feeling the way when entering the pond for the first time, in case there are any deep holes or deep mud.

DIPPING THE POND

The first reaction to sweeping a pond net through the water is usually one of dismay – there doesn't seem to be anything alive. But, like any other form of hunting, pond dipping requires a certain amount of guile, the right approach, and an eye that is adjusted to the very small size and the fragile delicacy of the quarry.

If circumstances permit, approach the pond cautiously. A light tread reduces vibrations in the ground which may send creatures darting out from the banks towards the middle of the pond.

Marginal vegetation should be examined for adult forms of aquatic insects, such as dragonflies, which may be emerging from their nymphal skin having crawled out of the water on the stem of a plant.

Scrutinise the surface carefully for animals which live on the surface film, such as pond-skaters which stride across the water. Waterboatmen and beetles are likely to be seen just beneath the surface, along with water scorpions and water bugs.

The first few sweeps with the pond net should be made near the surface – quickly enough to scoop up any insects that may try to escape, yet not so quickly that the mud on the bottom is stirred up.

The largest white tray or bowl you have should be filled with about one inch of clear water, into which the contents of the pond net are gently shaken. At first it may appear that you have caught nothing but a few twigs and old leaves. If you keep watch the creatures will suddenly begin swimming. With no water to support them many animals and plants lose their shape and have the appearance of little wisps of chewed wool. When the surface areas of clear water have been swept, sweep the net between plants to collect the creatures that shelter there. Inevitably, this will stir up a lot of mud so the first two or three attempts are likely to be the most productive. Lastly, scrape the net along the mud surface, sweeping towards the bank so creatures don't escape into deep water. A stiff net of wire mesh is ideal for this task.

A pond net is a surprisingly selective instrument because it cannot scoop

Pond-net adventurers . . . pond life has a particular fascination for children.

up species such as leeches and snails which cling to vegetation. Short of uprooting plants, and bringing them out of the water to search them, which would be vandalistic were it not carried out under scientific direction, the only way to find these animals is to wade among the weeds and search for them.

It is important to do as much dipping as possible from the bank, so your feet neither stir the pond up nor trample the underwater or marginal plants on which so many animals live.

Frogs, newts and tadpoles can be caught in a pond net and must be delicately handled. On a hot day it is possible to stalk a basking frog or toad from behind and trap it between your cupped hands. Newts can be attracted into the bank from the centre of the pond by tying small worms to pieces of thread. The worms are thrown out into the centre then gradually drawn into the bank. As the worms wriggle the newts will paddle in after them, to within reach of a long-handled pond net.

Not a lot of water is required for transporting specimens – a dense mat of weeds just covered by water is sufficient for a short time, and the insects will be less likely to be damaged by water swilling about. Sticks and stones should not be put in the containers because the movement may cause them to damage the specimens; a few leaves or weeds picked from the pond will make the insects feel at home and give them a little shelter. Polythene bags carried in cardboard cartons are ideal for transporting specimens as long as there is plenty of air in each bag.

Intensive collecting can ruin a pond and decimate plants and animals. To protect a village pond, follow this code for its conservation, and ensure that other people going pond-dipping, particularly schools, are aware of its importance.

CONSERVATION CODE

1. Examine all larger species at the waterside and return them to the pond as soon as possible.

2. Take no more specimens than is absolutely necessary. Return those that are not wanted immediately.

3. Use proper containers to hold specimens; keep them cool.

4. If pond-dipping in a party, make one person responsible for the care of all specimens.

5. Put back in their original positions any stones overturned for examination.

6. Return any water plants that have been taken out of the pond for examination.

7. Avoid trampling the margins of the pond and stirring up the water.

8. On arrival at your destination, put specimens in proper containers immediately; if left in small containers in a warm room they may die quickly.

9. Return the specimens to the same pond as soon as possible; don't wash them down the sink.

FLORA AND FAUNA OF BRITISH PONDS

CRACK WILLOW
(Salix fragilis)
Tallest of the willows, growing up to ninety feet, it has long, slender, silver-green leaves and is named because its twigs can be broken with a loud snap.

HERON *(Ardea cinerea)*
Undisturbed ponds are a source of food for herons which range far and wide in search of small fish, eels, and rodents. The heron flies awkwardly, head drawn back and legs trailing, and is often seen standing on one leg in the shallows.

OSIER *(Salix viminalis)*
Willow shrub that grows on fertile soil near the water's edge; formerly was cropped for wands with which baskets were made.

KINGCUP *(Caltha palustris)*
Also known as marsh marigold, it blooms with masses of yellow, buttercup-like flowers in spring and early summer; grows to about twelve inches.

WATER FORGET-ME-NOT
(Myosotis scorpioides)
Grows in dense mats on shady banks of ponds; flowers early summer and again later on.

REED CANARY-GRASS *(Phalaris arundinacea)* Similar to a reed, grows on pond margins and strengthen banks.

COMMON REED *(Phragmites communis)* A true grass, it grows in depths of four feet and attains heights of fourteen feet.

MOORHEN *(Gallinula chloropus)* Takes readily to a village pond and will breed there; when alarmed sinks into the water, only its bill showing.

WHITE WATER-LILY *(Nymphaea alba)* Characteristic floating-leaved plant.

YELLOW WATER-LILY *(Nuphar lutea)* Anchored to the bottom by huge rhizomes.

35

COOT *(Fulica atra)*
Favours large, open
ponds with dense
cover where it builds
nests that float or rest
on half-submerged
branches; aggressive,
it eats shoots, seeds,
tadpoles, nymphs and
insects.

WHITE WILLOW *(Salix alba)*
One of many types of willow, all favouring dampish soil, it has long pointed leaves and grows into a large tree that has a life span of about fifty years; grows easily from cuttings.

ALDER *(Alnus glutinosa)*
Growing sometimes in the water, its dense foliage is good cover for birds and its roots help to stabilise the banks against erosion.

SOFT RUSH *(Juncus effusus)*
Grows in huge clumps along the banks; its shiny, smooth stems are spiky and tough; in the old days its flowers, which emerge in clusters during June, were split open to make wicks for rush lights.

WATER CROWFOOT
(Ranunculus aquatilis)
Member of the buttercup family, its white flowers appear in May and June.

DUCKWEED *(Lemna spp)*
Spreads rapidly and creates heavy shade; can cover a pond like a carpet; good food for ducks.

37

MUTE SWAN *(Cygnus olor)*
One of the world's heaviest flying birds
and Britain's only resident swan, it does
well on ponds with plenty of
swimming room and is very tame.

MEADOWSWEET
(Filipendula ulmaria)
Sweet-scented white flowers appear in
dense clusters in June and cover the
pond banks; grows to between two and
four feet high; medieval house-holders
scattered it on the floor with rushes for
its fragrance.

GREAT WILLOW-HERB
(Epilobium hirsutum)
Hairy-leaved plant that grows up to six
feet; flowers June to August; its seeds
blow away in the wind, like cotton.

BROAD-LEAVED
PONDWEED
*(Potamogeton
natans)*
Abundant in ponds,
its upper leaves are
leathery and smooth
while its submerged
lower leaves are
narrow and delicate;
dies in winter but
reappears in spring.

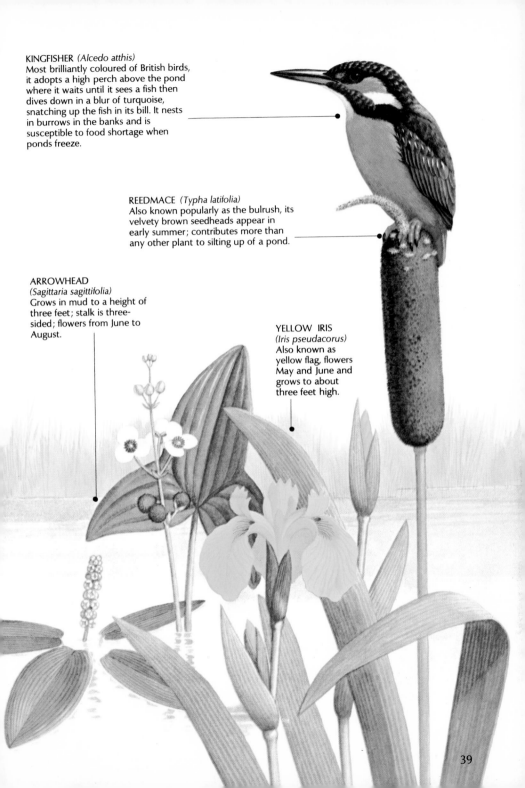

KINGFISHER *(Alcedo atthis)*
Most brilliantly coloured of British birds,
it adopts a high perch above the pond
where it waits until it sees a fish then
dives down in a blur of turquoise,
snatching up the fish in its bill. It nests
in burrows in the banks and is
susceptible to food shortage when
ponds freeze.

REEDMACE *(Typha latifolia)*
Also known popularly as the bulrush, its
velvety brown seedheads appear in
early summer; contributes more than
any other plant to silting up of a pond.

ARROWHEAD
(Sagittaria sagittifolia)
Grows in mud to a height of
three feet; stalk is three-
sided; flowers from June to
August.

YELLOW IRIS
(Iris pseudacorus)
Also known as
yellow flag, flowers
May and June and
grows to about
three feet high.

MALLARD DRAKE
(Anas platyrhyncos)
Although it is familiar in town ponds, the mallard is a wild duck. It feeds by up-ending and 'dabbling' – scooping up seeds, small insects, and stems of water plants beneath the surface; the female (seen at right) is a drab brown; it seeks out country-side ponds for food and nesting places.

PURPLE LOOSESTRIFE *(Lythrum salicaria)*
Tall perennial that grows to nearly four feet on the banks, it has lance-shaped leaves and reddish-purple flowers.

FALSE FOX-SEDGE
(Carex otrubae)
Grass-like plant with narrow, cutting leaves and triangular stems, it grows in clumps on the banksides of boggy ponds.

GIPSY-WORT
(Lycopus europaeus)
Grows to about three feet high on the bank, small white flowers appear in July and August.

WATERCRESS *(Rorippa nasturtium-aquaticum)*
Grows in small dense masses in clean water; flowers in May and October.

BUR-REED *(Sparganium erectum)*
Forming large clumps on the water's edge, it grows to four feet in height and casts dense shade on the water but provides good cover for wild ducks which also eat its seeds.

FROG-BIT
(Hydrocharis morsus-ranae)
Floats on the surface in rosettes, the undersides of its leaves harbouring many animals on which fish feed; buds sink to the bottom in autumn and reappear in spring.

WATER VOLE *(Aricola amphibius)*
Often wrongly called the water rat, it grows to eight inches and has a blunter snout than that of a rat and usually swims under the surface; builds a nest of grass or rushes in a burrow in the bank and after swimming can often be seen sitting on the bank grooming its fur or eating a piece of water plant.

DRAGONFLY *(Aeshna juncea)*
One of the largest of the twenty-seven species of dragonfly in Britain, it hawks far and wide in search of insects such as flies and butterflies for food. It can fly at more than thirty miles an hour forwards, can hover, and even fly backwards. The NYMPHS attack and eat other animal life in the ponds, catching their prey by flicking forward their jaws which, like the bucket of a hydraulic excavator, are on the end of long, double-hinged booms that fold beneath the face. After one to three years in the water, the nymphs climb up stems of weed and emerge as adult dragonflies that live only a few weeks.

SALLOW *(Salix caprea)*
Type of willow that grows very quickly from cuttings, is host to many native insects which attract birds, and is ideal for planting as shelter.

COMMON CLUB-RUSH
(Scirpus lacustris)
Often mistaken for the bulrush, it grows stiffly erect to a height of ten feet and sends out large, pulpy, underground stems that spread horizontally through the mud in all directions.

WATER SHREW *(Neomys fodiens)*
Lives in long tunnels in the banks which are so narrow that the shrew's fur is dried as it squeezes through; feeds on snails, insects, fish, and even frogs which it sometimes leaps out of the water to catch; swims well and walks on the bottom.

MARESTAIL *(Hippuris vulgaris)*
Spiky plant up to three feet high; roots creep across the bottom of the pond sending up erect branches.

WATER PLANTAIN
(Alisma plantago-aquatica)
Grows in shallow water,
sending up leafless stems to a
height of three feet; these
flower from June to August;
roots are edible when dried.

WATER STARWORT
(Callitriche stagnalis)
Enriches water with oxygen
and provides shelter for small
creatures; its leaves vary in
shape.

43

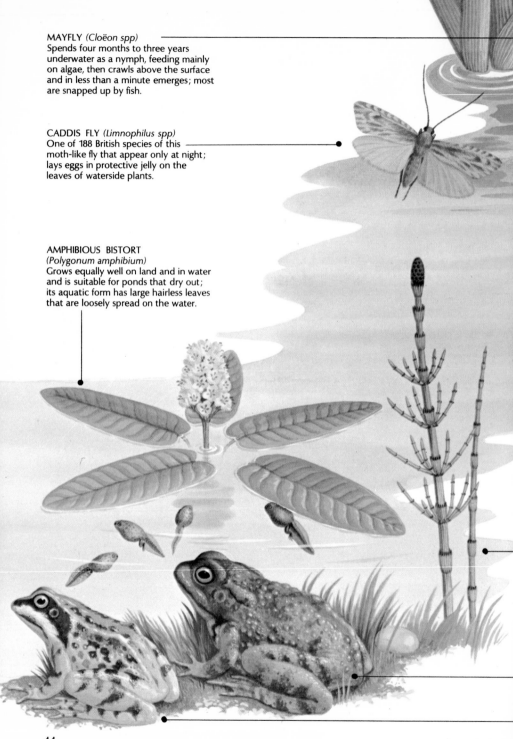

MAYFLY *(Cloëon spp)*
Spends four months to three years
underwater as a nymph, feeding mainly
on algae, then crawls above the surface
and in less than a minute emerges; most
are snapped up by fish.

CADDIS FLY *(Limnophilus spp)*
One of 188 British species of this
moth-like fly that appear only at night;
lays eggs in protective jelly on the
leaves of waterside plants.

AMPHIBIOUS BISTORT
(Polygonum amphibium)
Grows equally well on land and in water
and is suitable for ponds that dry out;
its aquatic form has large hairless leaves
that are loosely spread on the water.

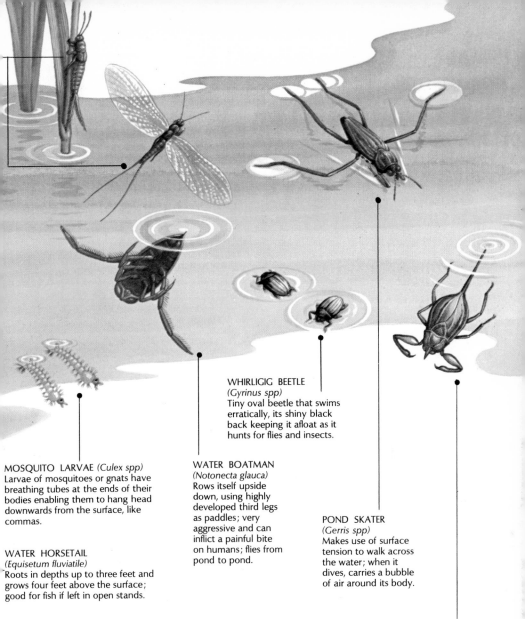

WHIRLIGIG BEETLE
(Gyrinus spp)
Tiny oval beetle that swims
erratically, its shiny black
back keeping it afloat as it
hunts for flies and insects.

MOSQUITO LARVAE *(Culex spp)*
Larvae of mosquitoes or gnats have
breathing tubes at the ends of their
bodies enabling them to hang head
downwards from the surface, like
commas.

WATER BOATMAN
(Notonecta glauca)
Rows itself upside
down, using highly
developed third legs
as paddles; very
aggressive and can
inflict a painful bite
on humans; flies from
pond to pond.

POND SKATER
(Gerris spp)
Makes use of surface
tension to walk across
the water; when it
dives, carries a bubble
of air around its body.

WATER HORSETAIL
(Equisetum fluviatile)
Roots in depths up to three feet and
grows four feet above the surface;
good for fish if left in open stands.

WATER SCORPION
(Nepa cinerea)
Sits motionless on
water plants in shallow
water, its breathing
tube reaching up to
the surface, then
pounces on small
water insects.

COMMON TOAD *(Bufo bufo)*
Visits ponds in March and April to
lay strings of eggs that are intertwined
among submerged stems;
distinguished from the frog by
coarser, drier, wartier skin and more
squat shape; its life span is ten years.

COMMON FROG *(Rana temporaria)*
The only native British frog, it is no
longer common because of chemical
pollution and loss of habitat; lays
clouds of spawn in spring which
floats to the surface in a mass of jelly.
Tadpoles reach dry land in July and
take three years to mature.

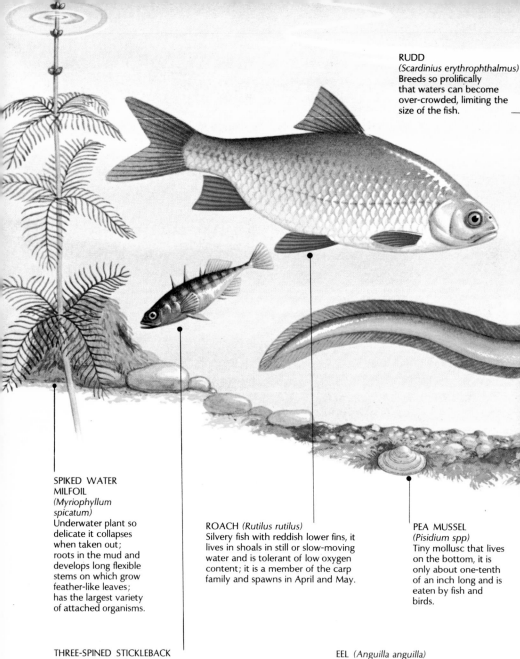

RUDD
(Scardinius erythrophthalmus)
Breeds so prolifically
that waters can become
over-crowded, limiting the
size of the fish.

**SPIKED WATER
MILFOIL**
*(Myriophyllum
spicatum)*
Underwater plant so
delicate it collapses
when taken out;
roots in the mud and
develops long flexible
stems on which grow
feather-like leaves;
has the largest variety
of attached organisms.

ROACH *(Rutilus rutilus)*
Silvery fish with reddish lower fins, it
lives in shoals in still or slow-moving
water and is tolerant of low oxygen
content; it is a member of the carp
family and spawns in April and May.

PEA MUSSEL
(Pisidium spp)
Tiny mollusc that lives
on the bottom, it is
only about one-tenth
of an inch long and is
eaten by fish and
birds.

THREE-SPINED STICKLEBACK
(Gasterosteus aculeatus)
Fierce little fish only about two and a
half inches long, it has an elaborate and
amusing courtship ritual that can be
observed in an aquarium; the male's
throat and belly become a brilliant red.

EEL *(Anguilla anguilla)*
Finding their way unerringly overland
from rivers and streams, eels live in
ponds for years until the urge to breed
drives them to head for the sea; in the
middle of the Atlantic they breed and
die; their larvae return to the coast and
become elvers which find their way up
rivers and streams to ponds.

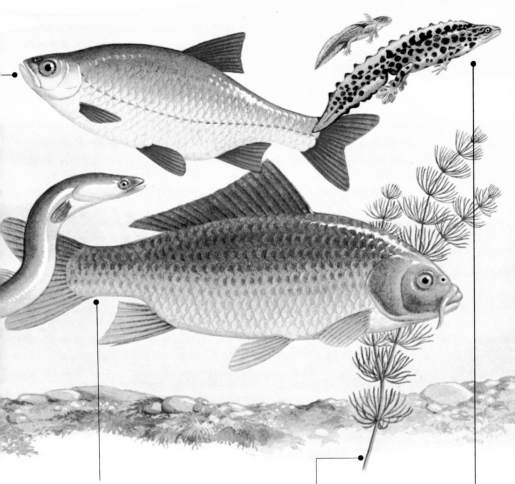

CARP (*Cyprinus carpic*)
Introduced as a food fish by the monks four centuries ago, it can sometimes be seen basking on the surface of densely weeded ponds in still weather; specimens of up to forty pounds in weight have been caught; in the wild the carp lives more than twenty years.

COMMON NEWT
(*Triturus vulgaris*)
Clumsy walkers but good swimmers, newts divide their time between water and land. Occasionally they shed their skins which float to the surface. Newt tadpoles take ten weeks to grow legs, then leave the water and may not return for two or three years.

HORNWORT (*Ceratophyllum demersum*)
Aquatic herb that grows beneath the surface; has no roots and anchors itself to the bottom mud only by little shoots; has bristly leaves and grows to a length of about three feet.

FRESHWATER SHRIMP (*Gammarus spp*)
Very active, swimming on its side, it
provides food for fish and eats detritus;
reproduces rapidly.

GREAT DIVING BEETLE
(*Dytiscus marginalis*)
Voraciously carnivorous, it attacks anything its own size including tadpoles and fish; before diving it gathers air on the hairs of its abdomen then, clutching this air bubble, is able to survive for long periods submerged, even when the pond is frozen over.

GREAT RAMSHORN SNAIL
(*Planorbis corneus*)
Freshwater snails differ from land snails in having eyes at the base of their tentacles, not at the end.

CANADIAN PONDWEED
(*Elodea canadensis*)
Introduced from North America a century ago, it spread so rapidly that navigation on canals was stopped; it is a delicate, fully submerged plant.

STONEWORT (*Chara spp*)
Highly developed family of algae growing beneath the surface, the stonewort is valued as shelter for fish and as food for duck; it grows in most pond waters; its colour is translucent green and its stems are delicate.

GREAT POND SNAIL (*Lymnaea stagnalis*)
Browses on algae and eats dead beetle larvae, small newts and sticklebacks; grows to $2\frac{1}{2}$ inches.

WATER SLATER or WATER LOUSE
(*Asellus aquaticus*)
Creeps along the bottom, or climbs slowly up water plants, feeding on decomposing matter; can swim skilfully.

HORSE LEECH
(*Haemopis sanguisuga*)
Swims well with undulating motion of its muscular body, grows to about six inches; devours smaller animals; harmless to humans.

CURLED PONDWEED
(*Potamogeton crispus*)
The wavy-edged leaves of this pondweed are delicate and translucent so they cast little shadow yet provide shelter for small insects and fish.

PERCH (*Perca fluviatilis*)
A thick-bodied fish with distinctive spiny dorsal fins, it eats larvae of aquatic insects, freshwater shrimps, and larger perch eat small fish such as roach and sticklebacks. It spawns in shallow water in spring and can lay up to 300,000 eggs. Its size depends on the size of the pond, type of water, and availability of food.

SWAN MUSSEL (*Anodonta cygnæa*)
Grows to eight or nine inches and has a beautiful pearl lining inside the shell; lies half-buried in the mud of hard-water ponds and filters algae through its gills.

CADDIS-FLY LARVA (*Limnophilus spp*)
When it hatches from its egg, the larva spins a web of silk around itself to which it ties small bits of broken plant, old snail shells, and specks of sand or gravel; as it gets bigger the larva adds to its case and never fully emerges from it.

49

5

Before you begin work recruit a volunteer labour force and make a careful plan. Investigate the water supply and deal with pollution. Use the right tools for the job. Let plenty of light get through to the water.

POND RESTORATION

PLANNING THE JOB

A pond is basically a simple hole, probably dug by hand for cows and horses to drink from. Then it was only mismanagement that allowed Nature to take over and try to claim the pond back. The principle of restoration is to tackle it with the same simplicity of purpose, and to allow Nature to take a strong hand without actually winning.

This picture of a round pond shows how the interests of the public at leisure, children doing field studies, and wildlife, could be balanced. Although the pond itself may be quite small it can serve the interests of each group ideally.

Public sector On the near side, where the lack of trees allows maximum light on the water, there is a pleasant view of the pond and the bank is skirted by open water which does not interfere with fishing, toy boats, or ducks that paddle up to eat bread. The grass can be lawned with neatly trimmed edges.

Educational sector Here it is on the left bank, backed by a belt of trees to protect the pond against prevailing winds. The vegetation is in clumps, so pond life is harboured but children can get at it with their pond nets.

Many village ponds which would seem to be in good condition suffer from over-management because people tend to think of the ideal pond as a clean sheet of water supporting a few ducks, around which is nicely mown grass. In fact this is the least desirable result if the pond is to be managed even partly for conservation. A pond that is denuded of plants attracts few insects, few birds, and, except in photographs, looks dull.

If you want a variety of wildlife around the pond, such as kingfishers, dragonflies, and flowering plants, it is important that this is planned from the beginning. But there is no reason why all of a pond should be made over exclusively as a domain for wildlife.

Conservation sector Public access must be minimal; if possible the whole area should be fenced (against boys and foxes) and include as much land as possible beyond the edge of the pond where scrub, trees and marsh plants can be allowed to grow. This will attract other types of bird and insect which will also make use of the pond. Narrow channels between the reeds should be kept open for ducks and pond life. Brambles and scrub can overhang the water so their seeds drop in.

Island A nesting sanctuary for waterfowl, and another opportunity for vegetation zones to establish; a sand or gravel landing place is ideal.

GUARANTEEING CLEAN WATER

Like everything in nature, successful pond restoration depends on balance. Almost any pond can be developed for several different purposes.

Probably the best time to do pond restoration work is autumn and early winter, although any time up to early spring is ideal if the volunteer workers can stand the cold. In autumn the weather is pleasant to work in, the water is not too cold, the sap isn't rising, wildfowl have not arrived, there is less material to handle because the trees are leafless, and most life is dormant, but if there is still some wildlife about it is unlikely to be greatly disturbed.

Unless fundamentally important jobs like removing rubbish have to be done, work on only one half of the pond in any one year. The vegetation on the remaining part will recolonise the other.

If material has to be raked out of the pond concentrate it at certain points and do not trample the margins.

Where it occurs, the zonation of plants should be encouraged by providing a shelving bottom. The diversity of wild animals that live in the pond depends on the zonation, and where it does not exist, perhaps because the banks are vertical, it can be improvised. However, good zonation is not a requirement in all ponds. Some natural ponds are very rich with only a few plants.

If a pond has to be drained to clear it out – by flushing a sluice, for example – do so during early autumn before the heavy winter frosts begin, leave some water in the bottom for fish, and fill it as quickly as possible.

Unless there is an inflow of water into a pond it could be a waste of time trying to restore it. The inflow must be of clean water, not water that is already polluted by industry, effluent or domestic sewage.

Many ponds are what can best be described as a bulge in a drainage system, and the cause of a pond drying up, or of pollution of its water, may be found some distance away.

At varying distances below the ground, water seeps through porous soil until it leaks out into a stream which eventually becomes a river. This is called the 'water table', which in most parts of Britain is tending to sink. Holes in the ground fill with water and become ponds when they reach below the level of the water table. Many such ponds have been left high and dry by the consumption of water for drinking and industry and by drainage of surrounding farmland.

An engineer from the local drainage board or river authority will be able to give advice on whether a pond lies above or below the existing water table, and whether anything can be done to restore a water supply.

Some ponds are filled by springs, which can be difficult to detect. One clue is that plants and animals tend to avoid the colder, disturbed areas where the spring water wells up from beneath the ground.

When the pond is filled by some kind of stream, ditch or gutter it will need an outflow. The water level of a pond can be raised by installing a higher outflow, which must be big enough to cope with flood water.

Pollution of a pond occurs in many

different ways and the cause is usually obvious. It is seldom necessary to have polluted water chemically analysed because the pollution will be self-evident.

The most likely natural cause of a pond becoming stagnant is eutrophication, where a pond has died from lack of oxygen brought about by over-enrichment from falling leaves (often coupled with lack of light) or uncontrolled cattle, ducks and geese.

The only cure is to keep the cattle or waterfowl out, clean out the dead vegetation, and cut back surrounding plants and trees to let in light, particularly on the south side. Eutrophication can also occur when a farmyard drain runs into a pond; the only cure is to ask the farmer to do something else with his effluent.

Chemicals from fertilisers and weed killers also leach into a pond. Although they do a lot of harm and inhibit the growth of wildlife it is most unlikely that the cure can be found at a local level.

A more easily resolved fault of farmers is the diversion of streams for farmyard water supply. By ancient custom no person owning riparian rights to a water supply can deny water to similar owners further downstream.

Severe pollution occurs when garbage is thrown into a pond. Poisons seep from lead, zinc, and other metals. Decomposition starves the water of oxygen. The pond smells like a cesspit, with slimy black or orange water devoid of life. The cure is to drag the stuff out and get rid of it in a proper dump. It will seem that the water must remain black and dead for ever, but in fact it recovers in a surprisingly short time.

Run-off from roads can severely disturb pond life, particularly after a long dry spell when rubber and oil detritus builds up and is washed into the pond with the first good downpour of rain. Many roadside ponds are fed by road water. A council may be persuaded to dispose of the water elsewhere, but then the level of the pond may fall. Alternatively, some kind of filter bed could be designed.

Pollution by sewage is usually detectable by smell, and by the richness of the vegetation growing along the route of its seepage. It usually results from inadequate or leaking septic tanks from nearby farms or houses and can be cured by laying extra dispersal drains or effecting repairs.

Much is made of the pH factor of ponds, which is a measure of the alkali and acid content of the water. However, this is no longer thought by some fresh-water biologists to be such a vital factor. An alkaline or calcarious water, of the type found on chalk, for example, is probably richer than any other. Acidic water has a low calcium content, does not support much plant life, but can support some animal life.

Generally, a village pond that has reasonably clear water, no rubbish, plenty of light, a minimum of fallen leaves and other vegetation on the bottom, and no taint of domestic sewage or farmyard effluent, stands a good chance of looking after itself. The proof that it is doing so is healthy plant growth, both in the water and along its shores. If the plants prosper, animal life finds its own way there quickly

TOOLS FOR THE JOB

Cleaning out a pond and restoring it is best done by hand, because machinery is non-selective and is likely to cause damage that could take years to repair.

Mechanical shovels, bulldozers and draglines do have their uses, particularly on a big pond, but they have a lot of drawbacks, such as the necessity to clean up after them and the need for a lot of room in which to operate. A dragline, for example, cannot operate near trees or other obstacles because it needs swinging room for its long boom, and its tracks churn up vegetation to such an extent that natural regeneration can be set back years unless sleeperways are used. A small hydraulic excavator of the type a council might be able to provide is more manageable.

Under skilled direction and given good weather, a team of twenty willing teenagers can do most of the heavy work required on a typical village pond during the course of a weekend. Volunteers might be recruited from schools, youth clubs, sporting clubs, scouts and guides, county naturalists' or conservation trusts or among friends and neighbours.

They can cut back the vegetation, leaving whatever is required to provide a habitat for wildlife, remove rubbish from the water, and dig out rhizomes. A local farmer might be persuaded to lend a tractor and trailer to take away vegetation; the local or district council can be contacted for disposal of rubbish and should be asked to provide a lorry on the spot so it can be loaded as work progresses. Tools can be borrowed from local farmers and the local council.

Waders (thigh high)
Very necessary when dealing with a long — neglected, deep-mud pond.

Crome (muck rake)
Its four strong tines pull out matted vegetation, saving back muscles and blisters because it is easier to drag than to lift; the longer the wooden handle the better.

Spade
A good cutting edge gets under reeds and loosens them for dragging out with cromes

Garden fork
Loosens reeds and rhizomes; useful for picking up floating material and wet leafmould because water is able to drain.

Heavy-duty rake
For levelling and spreading soil; heaping up waste for disposal.

Mattock (below)
An earth-digging tool with an axe-like cutting edge for cutting through roots, and a heavy-duty hoe for levelling soil.

WORK SAFELY

Great care must be taken when cleaning out pond rubbish. All workers should have tetanus innoculations. The organisers must know where a doctor can be found. A first aid kit and clean water should be at hand.

Hands can be protected with thick, canvas-backed industrial rubber gloves. Watch for bottles and broken glass when picking up handfuls of vegetation.

When getting to grips with a huge mass of rubbish, take a little bit at a time. If you are wading in the pond avoid falling over at all costs, not only because it is undignified but because you might fall on rusty iron. If the water is deep, chest waders are more dangerous should you fall in.

In water move slowly and get a good footing before starting work. Constant movement of the feet can prevent you sinking slowly into the mud. A probe should be made all over the pond with a sounding rod to check the depth and find unexpected holes.

Paper or plastic sacks are useful for disposing of small articles; through the local council a truck can be arranged to take it all away.

Waterlogged rubbish is easier to move once it has drained. Pull it up the bank until it is just above the water then leave it for several hours. Any insects or animals inhabiting it will take the opportunity to slip back into the water.

Young people should use saws and clippers, not billhooks which can slip even out of experienced hands, especially when wet. A slasher or an axe requires at least four feet plus the length of your arms for swinging room and should not be used in water. A person who is using one of these tools should never be approached – call him first.

Those not standing actually in water should wear boots (not waders) to protect their feet against cuts from tools. All workers who use tools should be trained in their use, and organisers should watch over inexperienced people or put them in the charge of someone who is experienced. Power saws and other mechanical tools should be used only by skilled hands. It is important to look out for overhead powerlines and underground cables.

Conservation Corps working on a pond.

Pick
For stone-breaking, lifting, levering logs, loosening clay before shovelling.

Crowbar
For levering boulders and heavy rubbish, breaking up hard ground, starting holes for driving stakes.

Axe
Wood chopper; when trimming, a saw usually makes a tidier job.

Slasher
For cutting out small trees, scrub and brambles; cut with an upward motion near the ground so the blade is not blunted by striking stones.

Billhook
For brashing and snedding (trimming tree trunks and cutting branches from poles), and cutting back scrub and bramble; many different types, some double bladed.

Bow saw
For felling small trees, trimming stumps, cutting down branches.

Gloves
Heavy industrial gloves protect the hands against broken glass and rusty steel edges of sunken rubbish.

Cement shovel
Raised edges handy for scooping out fluid sludge.

Drivall
For driving in stakes to make a temporary fence, or pilings to support a bank.

Wire cutters and tin shears
For cutting up rubbish into easily handled sections.

Clippers and secateurs
For tidying up loose branches.

Sharpening stone
Tools with sharp cutting edges speed the work.

Coils of rope
For hauling rubbish out of pond

Sacks
Paper, polythene and jute sacks are useful for disposing of rubbish

Coal scuttle or bucket
Handles porridge-like sludge easily and is comfortable to pass from hand to hand in a human chain.

Sledge hammer
For driving in metal stakes, or mawl for wooden stakes.

Portable winch, or block and tackle
Easily handles most tree stumps on soft ground.

Wheelbarrow
For shifting soil and rubbish.

First aid kit
Immediately bathe any wound in clean water, disinfect and bandage any wound, particularly if it has been in contact with dirty pond water, then seek medical attention.

When no local labour force is available to a village planning to restore its pond, volunteers can be arranged through the British Trust for Conservation Volunteers. The Trust assists and advises many local groups of volunteers and also organises its own volunteer work force. This group of several thousand young people is known as the National Conservation Corps, and will act as a 'flying squad' for the Save the Pond Campaign.

The young people devote their free time assisting in the management of areas protected for amenity and wildlife. During holidays and at weekends, teams of volunteers visit different parts of the country to carry out tasks in the countryside. They stay in village halls, or camp, and every team is fully equipped.

Typical tasks include clearing scrub, cleaning out water-courses, building footbridges and laying out nature trails. The work is supervised by leaders who attend special courses.

A special Ford Transit bus, with trailer and all the necessary equipment, including a punt and sludge-pump, have been supplied to the Corps by the Ford Motor Company Limited for pond restoration work arising from the Campaign.

GETTING IT STRAIGHT

When a pond is in very bad condition the first job is to remove whatever is causing the trouble and give it a chance to breathe. A concerted effort must be made to remove all rubbish immediately so the water begins to regenerate life. At the same time, any other cause of pollution, such as sewage or farm effluent, must be dealt with or the work will be in vain.

Some heavy articles, such as fridges or cars, may have to be dragged out of the pond with a wire rope and a winch. They should be left on the bank long enough to drain and let any animals make their escape; they will also become lighter.

Damage to the banks and surrounding vegetation should be confined by taking as much rubbish as possible out by the same route. Temporary steps or a slipway can be cut to facilitate the work.

Broken glass should be heaped in one pile so it is less likely to be trodden upon. Bottles found in ponds may have been lying there for decades, and some old-fashioned ones are quite valuable.

The rhizomes of reeds, which spread horizontally over pond beds in a dense mattress of bulb-like roots should be broken up and dragged out using cromes and forks.

In deeper water reeds will float once

CLEANING THE BOTTOM

1. When removing reeds don't try to pull them out. First free the rhizomes with a fork or a downward thrust of a crome, then pull.

2. In shallow water, dragging clumps of rhizomes along the bottom with a crome helps to remove the ooze on the bottom.

3. In deeper water a crome attached to a rope can be flung into the reeds then pulled out by two or three workers on the bank.

they are uprooted, and can be heaped into a raft which can be towed to the banks with a rope.

The material should be heaped up on the bank to drain and allow animals to escape. Then, when it is lighter, it can be forked into a lorry for dumping. When an emergent plant such as reeds is being eradicated from a pond it is important that *every* rhizome is removed or it will grow again.

Merely cutting reeds back with a scythe, or by dragging a wire back and forth below the surface – done in the main to clear waterways for navigation – is a waste of time in a pond because the following spring the reeds grow again denser than before.

Remove as much sludge from the pond as possible. The main cause of sludge, which turns water black and smelly, is leaves which fall into the water and decompose. Sludge can be pumped out and spread as fertiliser on a nearby field, or lifted out in buckets or coal scuttles.

When the pond has settled down again more specialised jobs, such as building up the banks, can be tackled by smaller teams of volunteers. It may prove useful to rake the bottom a second time.

4. If a punt is necessary, lean over the side and work the tines of the crome beneath the rhizomes then lift. The rhizomes will float and can he heaped up to form a raft which is then towed to the shore.

5. A chain gang using buckets or coal scuttles will soon empty a pond of ooze and sludge. The containers should be emptied on the bank so the water will drain back.

6. A tree-trunk or a bundle of poles can be used to scrape sludge out of a pond. The tree-trunk is laid along the bottom and held down by five or six people standing on it and balancing themselves with the aid of long-handled tools. A winch is then employed to drag the tree-trunk up and over the bank. On the bank, free-running water and animal life should be given time to escape so that only the mud remains.

59

REPAIRING
THE BANKS

Ideally, the banks of a pond should vary in steepness. In some areas they should slope gently, to provide favourable conditions for plant zonation. In other areas, steeper sides are preferable so that small mammals such as water voles can live in the banks. When rushes and other marginal plants become established along the edges of steep banks they overhang and provide cover.

Varied steepness is also desirable from an amenity point of view, because gently sloping banks and shallow water is ideal for children collecting pond specimens, while steeper banks low to the water are appreciated by villagers who come to fish, or feed the ducks. Very steep and high banks combined with water more than a foot or so in depth should be avoided at all costs.

In many ponds the banks have deteriorated and need rebuilding, or else it is necessary to cut them back to increase the area of the water and introduce a more gentle slope.

A sloping edge and gradually deepening water creates ideal conditions for plants, and is no danger to children. Ducks can come ashore but are inclined to ruin the vegetation, causing bare mud, in which case a layer of gravel can be laid down over a small part of it.

A steep edge is least desirable for conservation unless it is overhung by brambles and bankside plants which provide cover for duck and insects.

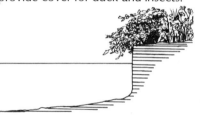

When the bank is high, and steep above the water as well as below, it presents a danger to children who can easily fall in and find no way out. It can

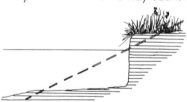

be improved by sloping the upper bank as shown, tipping the soil into the water to make it shallower.

An alternative way to improve a vertically sided pond is to dig a trench around the bank so that emergent plants such as reeds can be rooted just below the surface.

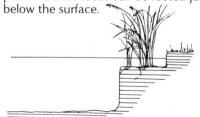

To make a bank safer for children, and at the same time create a shallow-water bed for emergent plants, a ledge can be constructed using a horizontal pole held in place with stakes. Soil taken from the bank is packed behind the pole which acts as a low retaining wall. If the soil is gravelly it may be necessary to dig it a little deeper and cover it with topsoil from another source.

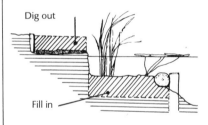

The simplest way of retaining banks is to build a low wall of bags filled with soil. If the bags are made of organic material, such as jute, they will eventually rot away. Or plants can be rooted in holes in the sacking. The area behind the wall of sacks is then filled in with gravel or rubble, and seeds are sown in a layer of topsoil.

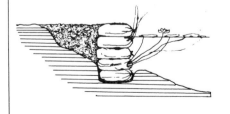

Piling can be constructed with poles driven into the ground shoulder-to-shoulder. Oak or elm is best, but willow will do if it is first de-barked so it won't root itself and begin to grow. The wood should not be creosoted as the pond would be polluted.

Banks can also be retained with poles held in position by stakes. If they are

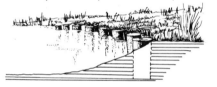

prominent and likely to be vandalised they should be bound with wire and staples. A hole in which to drive the stake (de-barked if it is willow) can be started with a crowbar, then the stake driven home with a sledge hammer or a drivall. The stake should be driven down until it reaches a firm base.

When a pond is being used for a lot of field studies and the margins are likely to be trampled, causeways or little piers can be constructed using poles and stakes in-filled with soil or gravel.

REPAIRING
A DAM

A pond that was made originally by damming a small stream can be ruined if the bank allows water to seep away. The tunnels made by water voles can soon start a leak.

This can be cured to some extent by digging a narrow trench in the bank and installing a barrier of butyl sheets or concrete. Joins in material used must be carefully sealed.

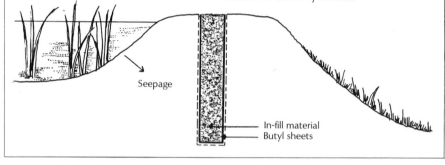

Seepage

In-fill material
Butyl sheets

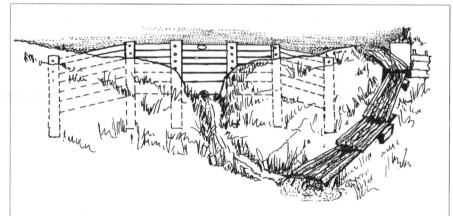

When a breach or hole in a bank has to be repaired, or a new outlet pipe installed to raise the water level, it may be necessary to divert the outlet temporarily by digging a sluice, or to construct a temporary coffer dam. Stout posts and planks will hold the water back long enough for concrete to set. Dam-repair requires an engineer's expert advice.

The breach itself can be repaired with concrete, or by building the equivalent of a second coffer dam and filling between the two with gravel, concrete, or impacted soil. A wide pipe of plastic or concrete – obtainable from a county roads depot – should be installed at the required height. Its diameter must be large enough to cope easily with the outflow, even after rainy weather when water is likely to pass through much more rapidly. A rule of thumb when building dams is that the width must equal the height, and if it is built only of earth, the width of the base must be five times the height.

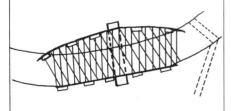

When the outflow of a pond merely needs to be tidied up, a yoke of concrete can be laid to hold an outlet pipe in position. The height of the pipe is critical because it controls the water level of the entire pond.

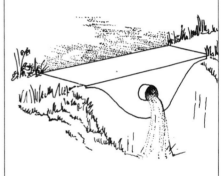

To prevent further erosion of the bank, the fall of water from the outlet pipe should be broken by heaped-up rocks or stakes.

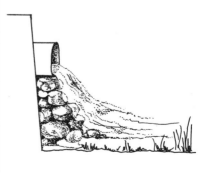

LETTING IN THE LIGHT

As much light as possible should be able to get to the pond, even if this means removing trees. Light is the basic fuel of all life in the pond, because the plants which grow in the water release the oxygen and other gases that are used by other forms of life, such as insects and fish.

A densely wooded pond supports little life. But often the vegetation around a pond is only willows, osiers, hazel and other scrub which can be cut back over a wide area and the stumps removed. The ground flora can then be allowed to regenerate and mown, or managed so that selected bankside plants take over.

When a pond is overhung by only one or two majestic-looking trees it is a pity to fell them because they happen to stand on the south side of the pond and block the light. The cost of keeping them may be more frequent cleaning of the bottom mud in the pond, or the lopping of one or two branches. There is no doubt, however, that when light in a pond is rationed, so the proportion of wildlife that inhabits it is limited accordingly.

As willows were frequently planted around village ponds to provide a source of withies which had many practical uses, they overshadow the pond now only because they have not been cropped. These 'pollard' willows are recognised by very thick trunks which, from a height of four to eight feet, sprout into dozens of smaller stems.

Although it must have light, a pond also benefits from shelter. A belt of trees left standing to protect it from the prevailing wind, and set far enough back so it neither cuts down on the light nor

A small hand winch will haul out all but the largest stumps on soft ground. A bigger tree is used as an anchor, and the trunk protected with wooden blocks. The wire should be placed as high up the stump as possible, to obtain maximum leverage.

Cut around the stump as deeply as possible, and continue to cut underneath with a mattock or sharp spade as the stump is hauled out. Bigger stumps can be hauled out by tractor or treated with chemicals.

drops leaves into the water, is an asset. A copse of smaller trees and shrubs, particularly berried species such as hawthorn and blackthorn, should be grown between the shelter belt so that the pond will be a habitat for many different kinds of woodland birds and insects. Willow and sallow are quick growers and easy to plant; like oaks, they support many species of insects, which in turn attract birds.

Felling a large tree should be carried out by an experienced person, and only after it has been ascertained that the tree must come down for a good reason. Stumps can be dragged out by tractor, or treated with a chemical such as 245T which makes them rot. Blasting is not recommended because it is likely to disturb the water table or the seal of the pond.

When cutting scrub with a slasher or a billhook, sweep near to the ground but finish the stroke with an upward twist so that the sharp blade is not dulled by contact with the ground.

When trimming branches from a tree, first make a cut with the saw on the under side of the branch then make a second cut from above. This prevents the bark peeling away as the branch falls. Bow saws are sharp and need no pressure: long, regular strokes cut through any wood very quickly.

When pollarding willows, make the saw cuts as close to the crown of the stump as possible for the sake of appearance. A lot of irregular spikes left on the stump look untidy and do not encourage growth.

BUILDING
AN ISLAND

An island in the middle of a pond serves the double purpose of adding interest to the water and providing a sanctuary, not only for ducks but also for other forms of wildlife. If it is a natural island, different types of vegetation will become established on its banks where frogs, insects, birds and other animal life can exist without interference from human beings, dogs, or predators such as stoats.

Around an artificial island, graded banks can be simulated with upturned pipes or wooden trays filled with soil and set below the surface so emergent plants and floating plants can be rooted.

The island effect can also be achieved with rafts, floating ones moored to one spot with chains and weights, or platforms fixed to stakes hammered into the pond-bed. No stakes should be driven into a pond with a puddled clay bottom in case it starts a leak.

On a much-visited suburban pond, where waterfowl are continually being disturbed by walkers, traffic, and dogs, some sort of island is essential if they are to be encouraged to nest and rear ducklings. If they are not given some kind of sanctuary they will search for more peaceful breeding places.

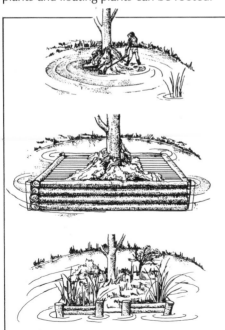

If an island already exists in a pond it should be treated like any other section of the main bank, and retained if necessary or the slope made more gentle, and part of it gravelled.

Frequently a pond has a living tree or a stump in the water. This makes an ideal foundation for a new island. While the pond is being cleaned out all the organic material should be raked around the tree or stump, and heaped up so it will drain. Then retaining banks of logs or earthbags (which permit the island to be practically any shape) can be built, and the island levelled (to original ground level or the tree will die) then planted with willows, rushes, and other species suitable for the banks of ponds.

If it is to be used by waterfowl they like to sun themselves on the south side, and to be protected by a low windbreak against the prevailing wind, so the vegetation and layout of the island should be planned with that in mind.

An island can be built with a circle of stout stakes and netting. Mud, leaf-mould, gravel and any other non-polluting filler material is then thrown behind the netting and finished with a layer of topsoil in which rushes and shrubs are planted. To create raised beds for growing water plants around the island, bagged earth or logs can be laid to create an underwater platform.

A platform on stilts provides many of the benefits of an island as far as birds and other wildlife are concerned, and does not suffer from the inherent instability – or the possibility of sinking – of a raft. If willow stakes are used and not de-barked, there is a possibility that they will begin to grow.

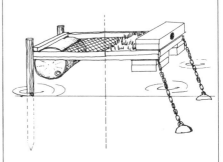

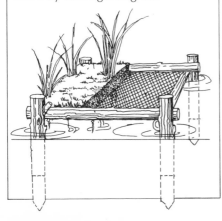

A floating raft is constructed like the platform with a stout netting stretched across the bottom and the tray filled with soil. This will keep the soil damp so plants do not dry out. Buoyancy can be provided by drums lashed at either end, steel tanks, or blocks of expanded polystyrene. Old telegraph poles obtainable cheaply through the GPO make good raft timber.

BUILDING A NEW POND

A village that does not already have a pond of its own can easily build one if there is a suitable site available. Unless the bottom of the pond is to be 'puddled' with clay in the old-fashioned way, like the bed of a canal, or is to be lined with concrete (which is expensive), the soil must be capable of holding water. A damp hollow may indicate a good site.

A source of supply is important. You can test whether the water table is high enough to fill a pond (in which case porous soil is not a disadvantage) simply by digging a hole in summer and watching to see whether it fills.

A small mechanical digger will cope with the job easily and can often be hired cheaply from a district council or a local farmer. A machine such as a dragline is expensive and creates a lot of mess as it goes.

Alternatively, if there are not too many houses near the site of the proposed pond, it might be possible to persuade a unit of the British Army to have some practice with dynamite and blast a hole.

Otherwise, it will be necessary to drum up an army of volunteers armed with spades, who can be assisted with a mechanical shovel borrowed from a farmer, and a tractor and trailer.

Small ponds for schools or gardens can be dug out in an afternoon and lined with thick polythene, PVC or butyl rubber. They can be filled with tap water, though the addition of rain water is helpful because it dilutes chlorine content.

When concrete is used it will be some weeks before the taint of cement is washed out. Otherwise, animal life will begin to arrive in the water immediately.

A pond can also be made by scooping out a wide area in a marshy depression that is fed by a trickle of water seeping down a slope, or by widening a small stream. This has the advantage of guaranteeing a good water supply. In effect the pond will be a head of dammed water. It is important to construct a sluice in the dam so the outflow of water does not erode it away and cause the dam to collapse.

When the pond first fills with water it will be very muddy, green, and pea-soupy, especially during the first summer. It is important to have the courage to persevere. If left alone, the problem will solve itself. It is brought about by the sun acting on the nutrients in the water and creating just the right conditions for algae to accumulate. The algae disappear as soon as the supply of nutrients is exhausted.

The cleaning up process can be accelerated by putting in a lot of rooted plants, such as water lilies or duckweed, which cut down the light and use up the nutrients. Native water plants can be purchased from dealers, and in a pond with a newly created bed can be rooted in bales of loam placed on the bottom at depths of about two feet.

Algae can also be killed off with chemicals such as copper sulphate. If administered in the right dose, according to the volume of water, it will not harm plants but might poison animal life. It should be done only with proper scientific advice.

Other plants such as Canadian pondweed, water milfoil and hornwort should also be introduced, and can be bought from aquarium dealers. To prevent them from floating, their stems should be lightly tied to small stones before dropping them in the water.

When introducing plants, look to see what species occur on other stretches of water in the neighbourhood. To some extent it is a process of trial and error, because some species hate competition. The right balance is achieved only by continuous gardening and experimentation. The criterion of success is not necessarily that of having more species of plants than somebody else's pond. It is a question of creating optimum conditions for Nature to do things her own way.

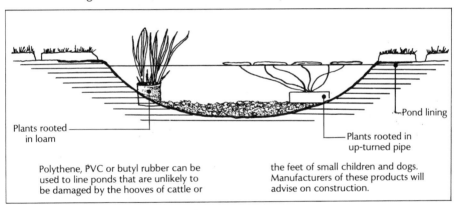

Plants rooted in loam

Pond lining

Plants rooted in up-turned pipe

Polythene, PVC or butyl rubber can be used to line ponds that are unlikely to be damaged by the hooves of cattle or the feet of small children and dogs. Manufacturers of these products will advise on construction.

To prevent the pond silting up, a square concrete box built just under the surface where water trickles into the pond will trap any sediment. The engineering of a sediment trap depends on the conditions of the pond. At intervals the sediment in the trap is cleaned out with a pump or a shovel.

6

Give Nature a chance without crippling her, attend to the surroundings of the pond; create the right conditions for wild or ornamental waterfowl, and fish, to inhabit the pond.

POND MANAGEMENT

SANCTUARY FOR NATURE

The first decision to be made about the management of a pond is – what is it being managed for? The question must be decided at the outset, and settled once and for all.

Some uses of a pond are incompatible with others. For example, if the pond is to be a focal point in the village, and all its banks are to be used by the public, the conservation value may be limited to the deeper water.

If the pond is to be managed for fishing, its banks will be constantly disturbed and trampled, weed will be unpopular because it will foul fishing lines, and only a few ducks – three or four at most – would be tolerated.

It does not take more than a pair of ducks to ruin a pond from a natural history point of view, because they eat the weed which is such an essential part of the pond's life-support system; more ducks can over-enrich the water with their droppings so that it goes green and scummy.

On the other hand wild and ornamental ducks are popular with the public, and the merry greeting of a flock of birds sunning themselves on the bank can be an amusing feature of village life. If the pond is to be managed for waterfowl, certain species are incompatible with others.

Swans, for example, may tolerate a few ducks but at certain times of year they won't stand for geese and will drive them off.

There are ways, however, of managing a pond so that a number of different interests are overlapped.

Given proper management, a limited

Pond 'nature point'.

number of ducks need not interfere with a carefully controlled amount of fishing. In turn, the fishermen must agree neither to take out weed nor disturb a sector of the pond that is set aside for nature conservation.

The right balance for any particular pond can be found only by patient trial and error. It must be a deliberate and calculated policy that is accepted by all those who have a hand in the pond's management.

A positive policy is also much more likely to be accepted – and respected – by the general public. A pond that is declared locally as a nature reserve gains status, not only in the eyes of local people and visitors, but also as far as highway engineers and planning officers are concerned.

Public respect for the pond and its wildlife can be encouraged by keeping them in touch with progress on the pond's restoration. A copy of the

BANKSIDE FURNITURE

management plan with a description of the ultimate result, and pictures of different species of plant and animal life that can be seen around the pond, can be mounted on a noticeboard nearby, as well as in the village hall or library.

The idea of special reserves where big game such as bears and tigers are protected from hunters is totally accepted by the public, and an imaginative display of why a pond is being protected for the sake of its wildlife should try to get across the same feeling of excitement and importance.

One way to do this is to arrange the equivalent of a nature trail. Because they are so small, ponds do not lend themselves to the 'trail' idea of numbered posts indicating stopping places at features of interest, which can be done ideally in woodland or along a riverbank of some length.

Instead, a pond can be treated as an entity and a nature 'point' set up to explain – with the use of pictures, diagrams, and a sketch – where the special points of interest can be seen. The display can be prepared by senior school pupils assisted by juniors, or by a natural history society.

It is important to concentrate on trees, plants, flowers, and insects that visitors are most likely to see – not just rare species that can be observed only a few times a year. People do not visit nature reserves and follow nature trails for lectures, but for explanations of things they can see, smell and touch.

The names of trees, nesting sites, species of plants and flowers, an underwater profile of the pond and restoration pictures can be displayed.

Once the pond has been straightened out and begun to recover from the scourge of sludge-pump and slasher, thought must be given to the surroundings. A pretty village pond attracts a lot of visitors, and it is important that the surrounding grass, heath or woodland is managed in such a way that it remains looking tidy.

If the grass is worn away from continuous pressure of visitors' feet, paths of gravel or concrete may have to be laid. Bankside paths sealed with asphalt could cripple pond life for months, because the first bit of rain will wash phenol (carbolic acid derived from tar) into the water and pollute it severely.

To avoid a 'city park' appearance of what is essentially a rustic feature of the village, concrete construction and billiard-table lawns are to be avoided. Banks shored up with pilings and retained by planks present a much more pleasing appearance than slabs of cement.

The most intense pressure on the banks will be at the positions where people stand to feed the ducks. In these

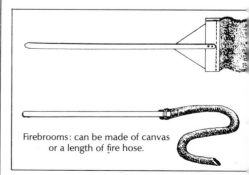

Firebrooms: can be made of canvas or a length of fire hose.

small areas some kind of paving stone can be laid, leaving intermediate stretches of bankside densely planted so people are not encouraged to trample them.

It may be thought that conventional park benches – vandal proof though they might be – are out of place around a pond in a rural village. Better-looking benches and seats can be made from poles and planks. Tree stumps make good park stools.

The best way of controlling cars is to dig a small trench and mound the earth into a bank which is then grassed. Posts painted white and hung with chains, or treated posts hammered into the ground until only six inches remains showing (just enough to halt a car) will also keep traffic in its place.

A railing to prevent prams and pushchairs from rolling in accidentally, to stop children from stumbling over the bank, and to guide old people who may not see very well or have good balance, is a good idea.

The railing can be of galvanised pipe, wooden posts and chains, or rails. It is important to have a rail or series of wires low down, to stop toddlers from falling into the water.

A lifebuoy attached to a coil of rope may serve some psychological benefit in reassuring village mothers that every safety precaution is being taken, but it is an open invitation to vandals. Unless the water is more than waist deep it will serve no great purpose. If a lifebuoy is used the 24-inch model is preferable to the more common 30-inch type used aboard ships.

A much more practical safety device is either a ladder, to help anybody who fails to get up the bank where the bottom is probably very muddy, or a long pole with hand grips so he can be helped to haul himself on to dry land. A rope quoit attached to a coil of lightweight floating line (like a water-ski rope) is very easy to throw.

Village greens tend to be cared for by traditional and established habits and unwritten conventions rather than by carefully planned management schemes. To alter such informal arrangements, or to impose regulations, however well intended, may encounter local opposition. But care and attention is frequently a necessity when established conventions change – as on a common when grazing is stopped and natural growth threatens to turn the area into an impenetrable jungle.

Bracken, woodland or heather near a pond may prove a menace during dry weather because of the danger of fire. Narrow firebreaks should be planned, and firebeaters provided so that people passing by can help control small blazes.

Safety equipment for a pond.

CONSERVING WILD DUCK

A village pond that is well away from neighbouring houses, and not disturbed too much by visitors or traffic noise, may attract wild duck. Mallard are common and might raise a brood of ducklings on the pond as well as use it for feeding. The Gadwall favours the eastern side of Britain and prefers more secluded ponds. The native teal may drop in to feed but will seek quieter conditions in which to breed. If the pond is situated near a lake or an estuary where wildfowl congregate, other species such as pintail may pay casual calls.

In winter, when conditions are hard and the supply of food is scarce, almost any species of wildfowl might be seen on a village pond, but it will not stay long. In some mysterious way the word goes out among the birds that food can be found, and they arrive en masse at a village pond then depart as suddenly as they have come.

If a pond is used regularly by wildfowl it may attract vandals with guns. If the pond is situated on a common or a green, this eventuality might be covered by a 'no shooting' bye-law. Otherwise, a notice should be erected to point out firmly but politely that the pond is a wildlife sanctuary.

Ideally, wild duck look for a pond which has sufficient open water for them to alight safely – a runway to land on. They like a well-sheltered 'loafing' area of open ground where they can sit and preen. The banks of the pond should be planted densely with brambles and other thickly growing plants to provide food, and the edges with emergent plants (not reedmace or common reed which will rapidly choke the pond). The marginal vegetation must provide food, and cover where duck can hide when they are moulting and unable to fly. This occurs during August and September.

Buildings and roads can be effectively screened by trees or shrubs but an area of ground between the screen and the pond should remain open so the ducks have plenty of warning of the approach of people or any predator. Ducks probably feel more secure if they can see danger approaching.

Their loafing area should be sheltered from the prevailing wind, and situated as far from public access as possible. The bank should have a gentle slope so ducks can get in and out of the water easily. Quick-growing trees such as willow, alder and birch provide suitable shelter; smaller shrubs should be encouraged to grow among them.

Wild duck are more likely to be attracted to a pond with an irregular, indented coastline than to one which is perfectly round. Drakes are territorial

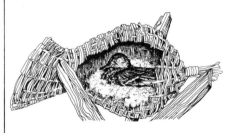

Basket nest and raft nest for wild duck should be placed well away from disturbance.

birds and are more likely to take up residence when they can take possession of individual 'bays' along the shore. The best effect can be achieved by taking out areas of vegetation to create the bays, each one separated by outcrops of dense reeds or – better still – by dense ground cover on spits of land.

Ideally, the bottom of the pond should shelve gently from the bank to a depth of about two feet for a distance of at least three or four feet. This area of shallow water allows emergent plants to grow, and provides the right conditions for ducks to feed on the bottom. A depth of at least four feet is necessary in the centre of the pond to prevent the pond becoming choked with weed, it also prevents the water becoming too warm on sunny days, and this lessens the likelihood of the pond becoming de-oxygenated.

Ducks will eat almost anything, but for their own sake their diet should be based on proper proportions of nutrients and roughage. Domestic bread does no harm, but if they get too much of it they will begin to suffer from lack of roughage. The main danger of relying on bread crusts is that feeding tends to be erratic – confined mainly to Sunday afternoons when there are plenty of visitors – and the wastage attracts undesirable scavengers such as black-headed gulls, as well as rats which prey on nests.

Barley is a wild duck's first choice, but beech mast and acorns, and other cereal crops – wheat, maize, etc. – are also good. The food should be scattered in the shallows over a wide area. As dabbling ducks can cause a lot of damage to soft banks, the food should be scattered well out. A pair of birds will consume about four handfuls of barley per day.

Sheaves of unthreshed corn, barley, oats, rye or wheat tied upside down to stakes so the heads are just beneath the surface are a laborious but nearly perfect means of supplying food to small numbers of wild duck and keeps them busy.

Early in March, the mallard will begin laying eggs at the rate of one a day. A sign that the female has begun raising a brood is when the drake is seen swimming about alone. When twelve or thirteen eggs have been laid she will sit, but the first clutch is unlikely to be successful if early in the season and she will lay another clutch. If the second batch is also unsuccessful, the mallard will try again. Before they can fly, the brood of ten will probably be reduced to fewer than half by weather, food shortage, and predators such as rats, owls, cats, crows, or pike.

DUCKS, SWANS AND GEESE

In some eyes there is nothing more cheerful than the sight of a village pond filled with different varieties of domestic and ornamental waterfowl. They are talkative, pretty and trusting. They need little care, keep themselves clean, and live outdoors most of the time. Children love to feed them with bread, and in early summer the sight of mother ducks proudly ushering their broods of fluffy ducklings is delightful.

Probably the most important requirement of managing a pond for waterfowl is to have the courage to keep numbers down, even if this means strict culling by catching ducks in a long-handled fishermen's landing net, or spoiling eggs as they are laid.

The number of ducks a pond will support depends to a large extent on what arrangements can be made in the village for their regular feeding, the state of the water and banks, and the size of the pond itself.

Grass is quickly stripped, particularly by heavy birds such as geese which graze on it. There is a very definite grass area/bird ratio which an expert can calculate depending on the type of grass and the species using it. Water running off feathers when birds come out of the pond makes the ground soft so the grass is easily uprooted. Vegetation in the pond, too, can be quickly stripped. Swans rip up whole plants. Green, scummy, smelly water is the inevitable result of too many waterfowl on a pond.

A gravel or sandy 'landing ground', where waterfowl come out of the water and drain, will save the surrounding grass from becoming threadbare. An island is essential if swans or geese are to be encouraged to breed because the security is proof against foxes and dogs, except when the pond freezes over.

Like wild ducks, ornamental and domestic species eat a great deal of vegetable matter such as seeds, leaves and berries, including the pips of blackberries, and chestnuts. If vegetation runs low, pond weed can be stored in buckets and thrown in as required, but this will be a short-term measure. Swans will even eat lawn clippings.

In summer, artificial feeding is not always necessary if the vegetation in the pond is healthy. Feeding can be reduced to only once a day, and omitted altogether for the first one or two days after a lot of bread crusts have been thrown into the pond.

In general, one handful of corn per bird, scattered in shallow water twice a day, is the rule. If there is any left over by the next feed they are getting too much, but domestic ducks will eat up to three times what they need. Special food such as poultry breeder pellets will give added protein during hard weather and the breeding season.

Feeding is best undertaken by one person in the village who might be appointed warden of the pond. When he is unable to do the job he can make alternative arrangements. If feeding is done on a rota system, with different people in the village taking turns, the diet will not be so strictly controlled.

Young birds are available for releasing from breeders in the autumn. They will need a week or so in a release pen to enable them to get used to their

Straw bales make a comfortable nesting shelter for geese.

surroundings before being released on the pond. Ornamental waterfowl will have one wing clipped, or 'pinioned', so they are unable to fly.

In very hard weather, food must be scattered near where the birds are roosting. They will be entirely dependent on the food they are given. Ice should be broken up and taken out of the pond so it does not damage diving duck.

Domestic duck

All but one of the domestic ducks were evolved from the mallard for egg-laying and eating. Through 4000 years of history they have become accustomed to having a roof over their heads, especially during cold weather. The different strains inter-breed among each other and with wild mallard, and appear in many different colourful guises which are very attractive. Any variety will do well on a village pond as long as the

ducks are fed and housed. As domestic ducks are reasonably tame there is no reason to pinion them.

The only domestic duck which has not evolved from the mallard is the muscovy, which in its wild state originates from South America.

Ornamental duck

Serving no utilitarian function, ornamental ducks are bred mainly in collections simply because they look pretty. Some are very attractive indeed, particularly the drakes, which develop brightly coloured courtship plumage. The brilliant colours are then replaced by a drabber plumage that helps to camouflage them when they are moulting and cannot fly.

The most colourful of ornamental varieties are the mandarin and carolina ducks, but they are inclined to wander away in spring.

There are two types of duck, surface feeders and divers. The common varieties are suitable for village ponds as long as they are fed regularly. A covered shed is not required, but good shelter from cold winds is essential.

Suitable surface-feeding ducks for village ponds are: European and Chiloe wigeon, European pintail, European shoveller, Bahama pintail, African yellowbill, and Philippine duck. The teal family should be avoided because they are smaller, and more vulnerable to predators.

Diving ducks do not walk so easily on land because their legs are engineered for swimming underwater, not standing on dry land. Nearly all the common ones are suitable, such as the pochard family,

STOCKING WITH FISH

tufted ducks, black and white diving ducks. Some of the more rare varieties such as the rosybill and the white-eye pochard, which are more expensive, would go well with domestic varieties because they can feed in deeper water by diving.

Species of shelduck, such as the European, South African , and ruddy shelduck, are big and colourful and not expensive but during the breeding season they are aggressive and capable of driving everything else off the pond.

Geese

The white Chinese goose and the grey Chinese goose are domestic varieties that do particularly well on village ponds. In fact all the domestic geese, including African buffs, pilgrims and Romans would be suitable. Of the ornamental geese, the Canadas, snow geese, and some of the grey geese, although more inclined to wander than the domestic species, would do well. It is essential that adequate grazing is available and that the edges of the pond are shallow enough to permit goslings to walk up on to the bank. Ideally, geese should be provided with an island or a fox-proof fenced enclosure.

Swans

Not good at walking because of their great weight, swans like a wide area of water with lots of vegetation. A pair of hand-reared mute swans released on a good pond would soon adopt a natural diet. Swans nest on mounds of hay or straw during the spring and are good parents. They are aggressive with other waterfowl.

Whether fish are to be reared in a pond for conservation or for sport is a question that must be decided at the outset. If the pond is to be a nature reserve, on quiet days large carp will bask near the surface with their fins showing, and if you are very stealthy, they will approach the bank and take morsels of bread dropped on the water. But if the pond is to be fished seriously, not only will the amount of fishing have to be severely limited to a privileged few, but the fish will become extremely wary.

If they show any interest, a possible compromise is to restrict the fishing to local children up to a certain age. Sections of the bank where vegetation is well established should be marked out for fishing, and small areas of water kept clear of weed. If indiscriminate fishing is allowed the banks will soon become trampled.

Unless stocks are seriously depleted it should not be necessary to insist that all fish are returned to the water. Fish reproduce so quickly that a few specimens carried home by a proud young fisherman will not do any harm. If transported carefully in a very large plastic bag they can be kept in an aquarium.

If fish do have to be returned it is important that it is done quickly, and in the right way. Fish should be handled only with wet hands, and great care should be exercised when unhooking them: if lightly hooked, hold the hook firmly and they will wriggle free of their own accord.

In general, no fish likes a pond with

a lot of gassy mud and ooze. If it is very muddy the water is likely to be acid, and produce a limited amount of food because there is not much oxygen. Only species with a low oxygen demand, such as tench or possibly common and crucian carp, could be considered.

If the pond is not too muddy common and crucian carp, tench, rudd, and perch should do well.

When the water is alkaline, and the bottom is clean, fishing conditions are optimal. A greater variety of plant and animal life creates more diverse conditions for fish, and most varieties of coarse fish will prosper.

Clumps of vegetation planted as islands around the fringes of the pond provide food for the fish as well as shelter. This is important during the daytime when lots of people on the banks alarm the fish through the highly sensitive radar-like pores along the sides of their bodies.

The best way of finding out whether a pond will support fish is to put some fish in it and see if they survive. The local fisheries officer (contacted through the local river authority) will be able to give advice and will know the sources of fish.

Basically, ducks and fish are competitors. But they are not incompatible as long as there are not so many ducks that the water is over-enriched and all the weed is taken out, and as long as predatory fish do not dine on too many ducklings.

When a pond gets a bit low on weeds and vegetation, as can happen during the winter, the fish can be fed with special pellets.

Pond fish

Common carp: Difficult to catch but highly tolerant of adverse conditions, it finds a lot of food in mud and can grow up to two or three pounds in ponds between half an acre and one acre in size; hibernates in winter and reappears during warm spells; takes paste, bread, worms, boiled potato.

Tench: A summer fish that takes worms, maggots, flake, paste and bread; it finds a lot of food in the mud and is tolerant of low oxygen.

Stickleback: Small fish that will thrive anywhere; can be caught on the tiniest hook baited with a fragment of worm.

Crucian carp: Chunky little fish that in a typical village pond grows to about six inches in length; it is very tolerant in all respects and adapts well to any sort of water unless it is actually toxic. Takes worms, paste, bread, maggots and flake.

Rudd: Attractive little fish that is very much at home in still water but does not like low oxygen or too much mud. It takes worms, flake, bread and maggots, usually near the surface.

Perch: Eats little fish and worms and takes very firmly so it is easy to catch; does not like unclean conditions and prefers a gravel bottom.

Pike: A pond must be an acre or more in extent for this viciously predatory fish which will eat practically anything – from spoon baits to frogs and small aquatic birds.

Eel: Not especially desirable in a pond but there is nothing much you can do about it: grows to three feet.

7

A village pond is an ideal outdoor classroom for observing and studying Nature. The children themselves can help a lot to keep the pond in a tidy and healthy condition, and by taking an interest are less inclined to cause unintentional damage.

FIELD STUDIES

LET CHILDREN TAKE A HAND

There are two good reasons why a village pond should be restored for the benefit –at least in part – of the local school. The first is that children can be mobilised into a work-force, and, when directed by their teachers, can help a lot with simple maintenance jobs during the course of a school year.

The second and more compelling reason is that a pond can be more easily adapted for study than practically any other natural habitat. For children it has a particular fascination because it is always fun playing with water. A pond is more likely to command their attention than, say, grassland or a hedgerow.

For teachers, a pond is the ideal outdoor classroom. Projects can be devised for children of any age group, whether they are five-year-olds drawing pictures of frogs with finger paint, or sixth-formers setting up elaborate observation records of the life cycles of species of dragonfly.

In most cases, a village pond and a

HOW CHILDREN CAN HELP

By far the most important role the pond 'classroom' plays is in social training. A child who has been taught how to net small insects from among the weeds, and has then learned about them in class, is not the child who is going to vandalise the pond – or any other natural environment – either intentionally or unintentionally.

Training children to be good observers and recorders of wildlife is halfway towards making them good naturalists and, by definition, good conservationists.

village school lie within easy reach of each other, so travelling time and cost is reduced to practically nothing, and visits to the pond can be more easily worked into a school day without trespassing on time that ought to be devoted to other subjects.

The practical value of a pond can be exploited for teaching in many different ways. The obvious subject is biology, because the pond's self-contained animal and plant communities are among the most fascinating of all. Children can actually catch specimens in their hands and keep them in the classroom or at home. The species breed rapidly, allowing complete life cycles of different animals and insects to be observed over a matter of days or weeks rather than years. Different zones and micro-habitats can be studied without having to move more than a few yards along the bank of the pond. The way different creatures have adapted themselves to life in the water – the water boatman's oars by which it rows itself backwards, the water scorpion's breathing snorkel – are vivid examples of similar processes which affect the lives of all living things.

Imaginative teachers can also make use of ponds for a wide variety of other subjects. For example:

History – investigate the origin of the pond and the way it was used.

Geography – show the past importance of the pond to agriculture.

Maths – map the outline and main features of the pond.

Geology – investigate the water table.

English – simple essays about the pond and its wildlife and scenery.

Chemistry – analysis of pond water at different times of day can show different pH factors as the temperature varies.

Physics – simple observation of a pond skater walking on water can lead to classroom demonstrations of how a razor blade can be made to float.

Art – insects and plants can be drawn from life then returned to the pond.

It is trite but true that the school children of today are the guardians of the countryside tomorrow.

Field work does have its dangers for the environment. Teachers should constantly assess the effect that their work is having. A pond can be denuded of plant and animal life in a matter of weeks if it is visited by a number of school parties in succession. Pond banks are by nature marshy, and susceptible to the trampling of feet, but do have a quick recovery rate. When a pond is visited often, part of it should be out of bounds so the vegetation can develop unhindered and gather its strength.

It is important that teachers play down the collecting instinct. Children's energies should be channelled towards observation of insects and animals on the spot. A small number of specimens can be removed to a classroom aquarium under the closest supervision. When the aquarium becomes overcrowded unwanted specimens should not be tipped down the sink but returned.

WINDOW ON POND LIFE

Pond creatures adapt easily to small aquariums because their natural habitat is still water. They can be observed more readily in small containers, and will exist happily as long as the water is maintained in good condition and not over-crowded.

An aquarium for the classroom can be made simply and cheaply with an old sink filled with tap water. It is important that a large area of water is in contact with the air – this area should be at least as great as that of the largest side. A large container helps to prevent rapid fluctuations in temperature.

For educational purposes, a glass-sided or plastic tank (not a goldfish bowl because the neck is too narrow and distortion by the glass too great) is ideal. To recreate as closely as possible the natural habitat of the pond, the sides should be screened with cardboard or black paper when the aquarium is not being observed for study.

The aquarium should not be placed in direct sunlight or the water will become over-heated and a scum of algae will grow on the sides of the container and need to be removed with a window scraper when the water is changed. Yet the water must be allowed as much light from above as possible, to keep the plants healthy.

A glass sheet or stiff plastic cover is important if the atmosphere is dusty, and if there are flying insects such as water beetles being kept in the aquarium. Pieces of cork or chips of wood should be placed around the lid to allow an air gap. If nymphs are being kept, the lid can be dispensed with and a branch or twig placed in the water to provide them with a ladder to the open air.

For safety, especially when children are taking a hand, do not place the aquarium near an electrical socket.

The container should first be scrubbed thoroughly, without using detergent or soap, then filled with about two inches of sand, pebbles, or mud. Preferably, this should be collected from a stream or pond, because then it will already contain nutrients and micro-organisms that help to form a balanced community in the aquarium. If the sand or gravel is taken from any other source, such as a field, it should be thoroughly washed in fresh water. Builders' sand and sand from the beach are unsuitable.

A few larger stones or rocks should be arranged in tiers to provide shelter, and, if frogs are being kept, some rocks should

---

STOCKING THE AQUARIUM

Plants
Canadian pondweed, pondweed, hornworts, duckweeds.

Animals that can be mixed
Water fleas, water lice, freshwater shrimps, snails, caddis-fly larvae, lesser water-boatmen.

Animals that should be kept separately
Water spiders, great diving beetles, greater water-boatmen, water scorpions, water stick-insects, gnat larvae and pupae, dragonfly larvae, leeches, sticklebacks, newts, frogs and toads.

ECO-SURVEY CARD

Name of pond: _____

Situation: _____

Length: _____ Max. depth: _____ Avg. depth: _____ Grid ref: _____

Water inflow: _____ outflow: _____

Approx. total number of waterfowl that use pond: _____

Name and address of owner (if known): _____

date: _____

Description:	Green	Common	Roadside	Field	Park
	Woodland	Quarry			

Access:	Public	Private	Right of way	School	Part public

Uses:	Fishing	Water sport	Picnics	Boating	Toy boats
	Game rearing	None	Abandoned		

Condition:	Clean	Stagnant	Green	Refuse-fouled	
	Oil-fouled	Vegetation-clogged			

Origin (if known): _____

MAP

Draw shape of pond, including any island, nearby road, house, fence, car park, path

Floating plants   Marginal plants
Emergent plants   Greensward
Submerged plants   Trees

Shrubs and brambles

Comments: _____

Name of Surveyor: _____

Address: _____

Please return this card to Save the Village Pond Campaign, Bell House, 111/113 Lambeth Road, London S.E.1.

SUBMERGED PLANTS

- ☐ Curled pondweed
- ☐ Rigid hornwort
- ☐ Spiked water mil-foil
- ☐ Canadian pondweed
- ☐ Stonewort
- ☐ Other :

FLOATING PLANTS

- ☐ Yellow water-lily
- ☐ Amphibious bistort
- ☐ Duckweed
- ☐ Water starwort
- ☐ White water-lily
- ☐ Broad-leaved pondweed
- ☐ Frogbit
- ☐ Common water-crowfoot

EMERGENT PLANTS

- ☐ Common reed
- ☐ Bulrush
- ☐ Water plantain
- ☐ Arrowhead
- ☐ Marestail
- ☐ Reed canary-grass
- ☐ Branched bur-reed
- ☐ Common club-rush
- ☐ Water horse-tail
- ☐ Other :

BANKSIDE PLANTS

- ☐ Kingcup
- ☐ Yellow iris
- ☐ Water cress
- ☐ False fox-sedge
- ☐ Soft rush
- ☐ Great willow-herb
- ☐ Meadowsweet
- ☐ Purple loosestrife
- ☐ Water forget-me-not
- ☐ Gypsy wort ☐ Other :

WATER BIRDS

- ☐ Mallard
- ☐ Mute swan
- ☐ Coot
- ☐ Kingfisher
- ☐ Moorhen
- ☐ Other :

AMPHIBIANS

- ☐ Frog
- ☐ Toad
- ☐ Newt

MAMMALS

- ☐ Water vole
- ☐ Water shrew
- ☐ Other :

MOLLUSCS

- ☐ Great pond snail
- ☐ Swan mussel
- ☐ Great ramshorn
- ☐ Other :
- ☐ Pea mussel

LEECHES

- ☐ Horse leech
- ☐ Other :

CRUSTACEANS

- ☐ Water slater
- ☐ Freshwater shrimp ☐ Other :

INSECTS

- ☐ Dragonfly
- ☐ Pond skater
- ☐ Water beetle
- ☐ Mayfly
- ☐ Water scorpion
- ☐ Water boatmen
- ☐ Caddis fly
- ☐ Whirligig beetle
- ☐ Other :

FISH

- ☐ Stickleback
- ☐ Roach
- ☐ Perch
- ☐ Eel
- ☐ Rudd
- ☐ Other :
- ☐ Pike
- ☐ Carp

TREES

- ☐ Alder
- ☐ Willow
- ☐ Other :

show above the water, or small floating rafts provided for the frogs to bask on.

Water from a pond or stream is preferable, but rain water collected from a downpipe is a good substitute. Tap water contains a lot of chlorine that is harmful to aquatic life, so it must be allowed to stand for at least two days to let the chlorine escape into the air. The aquarium should be filled to about four-fifths of its depth using a watering can, or by pouring the water on to a layer of newspaper so the sediment on the bottom is not disturbed.

Green plants utilise carbon dioxide and release oxygen in the process of photosynthesis; animals use the oxygen and release carbon-dioxide in the process of respiration. A proper balance between these two gases is vital. About one rooted plant for every four square inches of the bottom area of the aquarium should be introduced. To give them a chance to root, small plants should be tied down with small weights, or rooted in shallow water which can later be topped up to the required depth. A few floating plants can also be placed on the surface, but a great variety of plants in an aquarium is undesirable.

The plants should be allowed to settle for two or three weeks before more active animals are introduced. This gives the water time to adjust to room temperature. The water should be changed as seldom as possible, but must be topped up to compensate for evaporation. Large animals, such as sticklebacks, consume more oxygen and it may be necessary to aerate the water from time to time by squeezing a sponge into it, or using a bicycle pump.

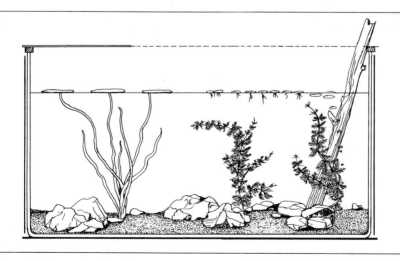

PROJECTS FOR POND-WATCHERS

Half the fun of learning about ponds is the practical side. Children learn by doing, and almost every aspect of the study of freshwater life involves difficulties requiring inventive solutions. The following are some ideas for educational projects which can be adapted according to the age of the children.

Rear a family of gnats

In summer the edges of any small body of water, such as a horse trough, a bird-bath, or a pool of stagnant water, are likely to contain egg rafts laid by gnats (mosquitoes). They are in groups about one centimetre long and look like patches of soot on the surface. They also occur in ponds, but are less easy to find.

The egg rafts can be scooped up with a spoon and kept in a glass jar or tumbler of pond water with some pond weed to provide oxygen. After a few days little wriggling larvae drop out of the eggs and spend most of their time hanging beneath the water by means of breathing tubes.

After about a week the larvae change to a pupae which breathe through two little ear trumpets on their heads. They remain on the surface until, one day, their heads split open and out crawl adult insects which fly away.

Make a profile of the pond

Two people are required, one to measure and one to record. The measuring is done with a string knotted or marked every ten centimetres and stretched above the surface of the water between two sticks, one pushed into the bank and one pushed into the mud of the pond so it projects above the water.

A ruler is then used to measure the depth of the water at each knot, and the types of plants found there, including underwater weed, are identified.

The recording is done on graph paper, with each ten centimetres of the measuring string represented by one centimetre on the paper.

A complete picture of a small pond can be built up in this way. It is important that the depth of the pond is first tested by an adult and that children are supervised at all times.

Making a profile.

Watch a caddis larva build its home

When a caddis larva hatches it spins a net around itself then collects fragments of stick which it ties to the net. As the larva gets bigger the case is made longer. When it is fully grown the larva changes into a pupa inside its case.

The pupa bites its way out, swims to the surface, and crawls on to dry land where the caddis fly pulls itself out of the old pupal skin, spreads its wings, and flies away. A caddis larva can be removed from its case by pushing gently with the *head* of a pin. If its case consisted of pieces of stick or plant stem, put long pieces into a dish of water beside it and the larva will begin to build a new case, measuring itself against the pieces before cutting the right length. If small glass beads or mica are provided it will make itself a transparent case.

Watch tadpoles change into frogs

When collecting frog spawn from a pond in March, take only a small lump. Put it in a bowl of water. When tadpoles first hatch they hang from the jelly and do not need feeding. When they wriggle free catch them in a spoon and put them in a small aquarium where they will live happily on aquatic plants.

At the first sign of the back legs beginning to appear, three weeks after hatching, they will need some meat – a very small shred of raw meat tied to a piece of cotton will do. The meat and the water ought to be changed every few days. The tadpoles cluster around it, and nibble.

The tadpoles will come to the surface more frequently and blow bubbles as their gills disappear. A floating piece of cork or wood should be put in the aquarium and one day the tadpoles will crawl on to it and begin to look like little frogs. At this stage the frogs should carefully be returned to the pond, as they are then very difficult to feed and are liable to die.

Keep sticklebacks and watch them nest

Sticklebacks are meat eaters and ought to be fed on water fleas, bloodworms or chopped mealworms which can be bought at pet shops. If you start keeping these fascinating little fish in January or February you might be lucky enough to see them making a nest.

The aquarium needs a fairly dense growth of plants and a gravel bottom. The nest is made by the male, who digs out a shallow hole in the gravel then carries in bits of plants and fastens them together with a sticky substance which he rubs on with his belly. He makes a tunnel in the nest and by doing a dance, attracts a female into it, then she lays her eggs.

The male stays near the nest, becoming aggressive and warlike as he chases away anything that comes near. In about ten days the young fish hatch and the male becomes even busier, catching the young in his mouth as they come out of the nest and spitting them back in again.

When the breeding cycle is over, return the sticklebacks to their pond.

THE GOSBERTON MIRACLE

8

For fifty years Lowgate Pit, a reed-fringed pond in the village of Gosberton, Lincolnshire, was used as a dump. The water was black and foul: nothing lived in it except rats. Then a small group of local people decided to do something about it. After three years of effort they were rewarded with a Countryside in 1970 bronze plaque. Now the pond is a gem of a nature reserve.

The Gosberton team (left to right): Dr Vincent Clarke, Eric Booth, Colin Smith, Les and Hazel Houldershaw, Jack Griffin, Ray Collier (Lincolnshire Trust conservation officer).

FROM POISONED PIT TO NATURE SANCTUARY

Gosberton (population 2500) is set amid the rich kitchen-garden farmland of south Lincolnshire. It has no village green, no park, only a graveyard. Straying off the roads is difficult because the fields, worth more than £1000 an acre, are ploughed to the last inch.

The pond, known as Lowgate Pit, originated as a brick pit about a century ago and was later used to water horses that pulled carts delivering groceries to local farmhouses. Then the horses were replaced by motor vans, and for the last fifty years the pond has been the village tip.

Les Houldershaw, a village joiner and undertaker, was building his own bungalow opposite when he was bothered by rats scavenging for food. On investigation, he found they came from the pit.

'It was the worst sight you could imagine,' he recalled. 'The water boiled with rubbish. It was so inky black you could write your name with it. Everything around it was dead, even the grass. There were so many rats that if you stood still for a minute, a dozen came out and played within three feet of you, like kittens.'

'Every sunny Saturday afternoon,' remembered his wife Hazel, 'we would see three or four barrows of rubbish being tipped into the pond. Farmers disposed of whole trailer-loads of old potatoes and flower-bulbs. Raw sewage was seeping in from a leaking septic tank nearby. And later we found 326 bottles that had contained Metasystox – a very powerful concentrated pesticide that's positively lethal.'

Work started in 1967. Les Houldershaw joined forces with his neighbour Tony Smith, a potato buyer, and joiner Jack Griffin whose workshop overlooked the pond. A keen angler, Jack Griffin planned to stock the pond with fish, and brought in fellow-fishermen Colin Smith, a home decorator, and Eric Booth, a petrol representative. (Jack Griffin and Eric Booth had trained near Gosberton for the Arnhem landing, were imprisoned together, then returned to the area).

Later, others lent a hand, including the village doctor, 'The place was simply poisoned,' said Dr Vincent Clarke, who lives near the pond.

The workers had tetanus jabs and had to beware of Weil's Disease, a potentially fatal type of fever passed on by rats. 'If anybody had fallen in they would have been poisoned, too,' Dr Clarke added, 'but fortunately nobody did.'

At first there was so much rubbish that falling in was difficult. Tons of old drums, bits of car, wire, and fragments of rusty metal were removed in a huge farm trailer. A section of bedstead was used as a grapnel with which to sweep the bottom. Every weekend for two years a bonfire burned in the orchard on the banks of the pond, disposing of rubbish. Forty pounds of rat poison were put down. The smell of the pesticide bottles made Les Houldershaw feel ill and faint, so he handled only a few at a time.

'The stench was so bad that when we stirred up the mud we had to move along the bank a bit and start again somewhere else until it settled down, . he said.

A small notice was erected to stop dumping and from that moment the problem never occurred again. 'People respected it,' said Les Houldershaw, 'but I think they thought we were idiots.'

'It seemed hopeless at the start,' said Eric Booth, 'and when we were still working with handkerchiefs over our noses after the first year it looked more hopeless.'

Jack Griffin knew the eel was always last to leave polluted water, and therefore could be the first to go back. When the rubbish had been cleaned out he put an eel into the pond – and it died. The small group of volunteers were then planning to chip in a few pounds each towards the cost of buying the pond for £100.

But after two years of work the Lincolnshire Trust for Nature Conservation became involved and offered to buy the pond for a nature reserve.

At the same time a new sewage main was installed in Lowgate, so that solved the leaking septic tank problem. The water began to clean itself up remarkably quickly. Another eel thrown into the pond survived – the pond was beginning to live again.

The Lincolnshire Trust drew up a management plan (see overleaf) and, to put things on an official footing, Les Houldershaw was appointed voluntary warden. 'The plan gave us all something to aim for – we knew what we were working for,' he said.

Somewhat sadly, the anglers kissed goodbye to their hopes of using the pond as a private fishing water, but they have no regrets. Jack Griffin, Eric Booth, and other villagers brought back weeds, frog spawn and once even a small oak tree from fishing trips

Forty-three carp, seven tench, forty-seven rudd and three perch, netted in local creeks, were introduced when the water was clean enough. Nettles, which had been chopped down to tidy the place up, were allowed to regenerate to attract butterflies. By 1970 the pond was getting straight and – 'Slightly with our tongues in our cheeks,' said Dr Clarke – their scheme was entered for a Countryside Award.

Justifiably it won a bronze plaque, which Jack Griffin went to the London Guildhall to receive from the Duke of Edinburgh.

Since then, vegetation around the pond has matured. The fish took to the water so happily that 500 small rudd were sold to a local angling club

Now, instead of rats infesting the area, a little water vole lives in the bank, and, if you sit quietly on one of the bench seats that Les Houldershaw has made, will come and clean his whiskers within a few inches of your feet. There are nesting boxes in the apple trees. An observation hut has been erected and a hundred people a year, from places as far afield as London and Liverpool, sign the book.

Pond weeds have been brought in on ducks' feet and every year new species of plants appear, to be recorded in the hut by Les Houldershaw. Orchids grow in the rough-cut grass. Every day village people, particularly children and old people, sit in the little nature reserve to watch the clear and tranquil water.

SYSTEMATIC RESTORATION

These three plans show the restoration plan for Lowgate Pit, Gosberton. It was drawn up by the Lincolnshire Trust for Nature Conservation which was asked by the villagers to advise how natural life in the pond could best be regenerated and managed.

The management plan includes such things as an area of nettles to attract butterflies, an absolute maximum width beyond which the fringe of reeds must not be allowed to spread because there would be a danger of its choking the pond, and brambles and briars which overhang the water's edge.

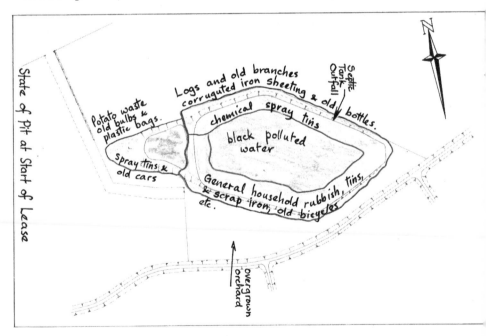

1. Before work started: mountains of potato waste in plastic bags, seepage from a domestic septic tank, black polluted water – the picture could not have looked much worse.

2. This plan shows what the pond looked like when the rubbish was cleaned out. Certain trees were carefully retained, the reed-bed had been cut back, and the area of water was more than doubled.

3. Meanwhile, looking ahead, this plan was drawn up to define exactly what they were all working towards – a nature reserve for birds, insects, fish, and freshwater life.

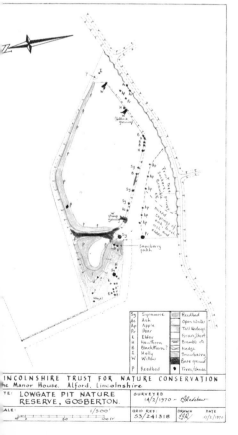

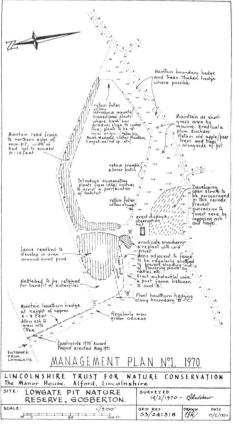

ORGANISATIONS THAT CAN HELP

Save the Village Pond Campaign will put organisers of pond restoration projects in touch with experts and advisers as required. The right organisation to help with any particular problem can vary from district to district. These are some of the conservation and amenity bodies whose local officers or representatives can be contacted through the Campaign headquarters at 111, Lambeth Road, London SE1.

Association of County Naturalists' and Conservation Trusts (incorporating the Society for the Promotion of Nature Reserves)

There are thirty-nine trusts in England and Wales, while Scotland is covered by the Scottish Wildlife Trust which has many branches. The Association co-ordinates the independent trusts and provides a number of services for them, administering funds on their behalf for the purchase of nature reserves. It is through the local trusts that the Association is able to lend assistance and advice on wildlife conservation and the establishment and management of ponds as nature reserves.

Trusts are established in the following counties and regions: Bedfordshire and Hunts; Berkshire, Buckinghamshire and Oxfordshire; Cambridgeshire and Isle of Ely; Cheshire; Cornwall; Derbyshire; Devon; Dorset; Durham; Essex; Gloucestershire; Hampshire and Isle of Wight; Herefordshire and Radnorshire; Hertfordshire and Middlesex; Isle of Man; Kent; Lake District; Lancashire; Leicester-shire and Rutland; Lincolnshire; Norfolk; Northampton; Northumberland; Nottinghamshire; Shropshire; Somerset; Staffordshire; Suffolk; Surrey; Sussex; Warwickshire; Wiltshire; Worcestershire; Yorkshire; North Wales; West Wales; Brecknock; Glamorgan; Monmouthshire; Scotland.

Biological Records Centre

Collects information on the distribution of plants and animals throughout the British Isles; gives advice on methods of recording the wildlife interest of habitats, and supplies recording cards and instructions.

British Trust for Conservation Volunteers (National Conservation Corps)

Provides facilities for young people who do practical work in the countryside under skilled guidance. At a nominal charge for labour, the Trust is in a position to contract for the cleaning out of ponds which have public access and a strong conservation interest.

British Waterfowl Association

Organiser of the Save the Village Pond Campaign, it promotes the conservation of all types of waterfowl and represents the interests of those breeding or keeping ornamental or domestic species; offers practical help and guidance on any aspect of the management of waterfowl.

Chiltern Society

Concerned for the beauty, history and character of the area of the Chiltern Hills.

Commons, Open Spaces and Footpaths Preservation Society

Known simply as the Commons Society, its objects are to preserve commons and village greens for public use, to advise on the securing and preserving of public open spaces, and to secure access to open country and to preserve footpaths. It can advise on legal questions arising from the restoration of ponds in such places.

Council for Nature

National representative body for the voluntary natural history movement in Britain; acts on behalf of naturalists to further the study of nature.

Council for the Protection of Rural England
Council for the Protection of Rural Wales
Association for the Preservation of Rural Scotland

Organise concerted action to improve, protect and preserve the rural scenery and amenities of the countryside, its town and villages, and act as a centre for producing advice and information.

Countryside Commission

Formerly the National Parks Commission, it is a Government body with wide-ranging responsibilities including the provision of information services about the countryside, statutory advice on proposals affecting the beauty of the countryside and its use for open-air recreation, and giving grants or loans to help non-public bodies carry out projects. Can also give grants (up to 75 per cent) to local authorities for country parks and picnic sites.

National Association of Local Councils

Protects and promotes the interests, rights, functions and privileges of local councils in England and Wales, and develops the social cultural and recreational life of parishes and villages. There is a county association of local councils in each county.

Nature Conservancy Council

Provides scientific advice on the conservation and management of the natural flora and fauna of Britain; establishes, maintains and manages nature reserves of national importance.

River Authorities (England and Wales)

Maintain rivers in connection with matters of drainage, land use, flood prevention, pollution of water, inland fisheries, conservation of water resources; records are kept of ground-water levels. There are twenty-nine individual river authorities.

Royal Society for the Protection of Birds

Encourages better conservation of wild birds and their habitats, provides material and advice to schools·and young people; manages nature reserves of national importance for birds.

Wildfowlers' Association of Great Britain and Ireland

Assists in the preservation and conservation of wildlife, particularly wildfowl; suppresses irresponsible and unlawful killing of wild birds and wild animals; promotes the interests of wildfowlers.

ACKNOWLEDGEMENTS

The author acknowledges with grateful thanks the
assistance of the following people who were
consulted during the preparation of this book:

Ursula Bowen MA MIBiol

Jo Burgon BA

Ian Campbell LIB

John Clarke MA BCL

John Clegg

Ray Collier

Wilf Dawson

Don Gresswell

Ian Grey

John Hall

Les Houldershaw

Richard Jennings

Franklyn Perring PhD

Oliver Rackham PhD

Miss F Stevens

David Streeter BSc

Alan Stubbs BSc

John Swift BA

Bernard Venables

The author acknowledges his debt to the following books and articles which were among many consulted:

Freshwater Animals Gwen Allen, Joan Denslow (Oxford University Press).

A Country Parish A. W. Boyd (Collins).

A Handbook of Water Plants Eva M. Busche (Warne).

A Guide to the Law of Commons Ian Campbell LIB (The Commons Society).

Tomorrow's Countryside Garth Christian (John Murray).

Colonising a Pond John Clegg (Wildlife and the Countryside, issue 268).

A Plea for Village Ponds John Clegg (The New Scientist, Volume 8).

The Freshwater Life of the British Isles John Clegg (Warne).

The Secret World of the Pond John Clegg (Wolfe).

Archaeology in the Field O. G. S. Crawford (Phoenix House).

Commons and Village Greens D. R. Denman, R. A. Roberts, H. J. F. Smith (Leonard Hill).

Everyman's Nature Reserve, Ideas for Action edited by Eve Dennis (David & Charles).

Pond-Life W. Engelhardt (Burke Books).

Pond Life R. L. E. Ford (Adam and Charles Black).

A Gravel Pit Wildfowl Reserve Jeffery Harrison (Wildfowlers' Association of Great Britain and Ireland).

A Wealth of Wildfowl Jeffery Harrison (Corgi).

The Making of the English Landscape W. G. Hoskins (Pelican).

The Common Lands of England and Wales W. G. Hoskins, L. Dudley Stamp (Collins).

Ornamental Waterfowl Lt-Col A. A. Johnson, W. H. Payn (H. F. and G. Witherby).

Ponds and Lakes T. T. Macan (Allen & Unwin).

Preserving the Ponds Alan Major (The Village, Volume 26, Number 3).

The Dark World of Witches Eric Maple (Pan).

A Guide to the Study of Freshwater Biology James G. Needham, Paul R. Needham (Constable).

The Practical Guide to Ornamental Waterfowl and Exotic Garden Birds John and Phyllis Parker (Arco).

Land and Leisure J. Allan Patmore (Pelican).

Dewponds in Fable and Fact Alfred J. Puglsey (Country Life).

Fresh-Water Life: Cold-Water Aquaria Mark R. D. Seaward (Universities Federation for Animal Welfare).

Book of British Birds (Drive Publications).

Book of the British Countryside (Drive Publications).

Know Your Wildfowl Food Plants (Wildfowlers' Association of Great Britain and Ireland).